THE NEW WILDERNESS

What We Know About Space

THE NEW WILDERNESS

What We Know About Space

BY WILLARD E. WILKS

DAVID McKAY COMPANY, INC.

New York

THE NEW WILDERNESS

What We Know About Space

LIBRARY OF CONGRESS CATALOG CARD NUMBER: 63-13169

MANUFACTURED IN THE UNITED STATES OF AMERICA

VAN REES PRESS • NEW YORK

FOR ELLEN AND DIANA,
WHO MAY SOME DAY MAKE THE TRIP

INTRODUCTION

SETTING down the final word in a book brings perhaps the greatest moment of joy that an author experiences in production of the work. The task at last accomplished, he turns with some relish to the matter of putting down a few words of introduction and acknowledgment. And with release from the discipline of hewing strictly to words which contribute to the theme of the book, it is difficult to resist the temptation to throw just a few words around with somewhat less than the restraint exercised formerly.

With these thoughts in mind, and with the desire to misuse no words, let it be plainly stated that this book could not have been produced without award by the Sloan and Rockefeller foundations of a fellowship for a year's work at Columbia University. Establishment and support of the Advanced Science Writing Fellowship is helping fill an ever-growing and critical need for more science reporting for the layman in this nuclear Space Age. The products of science and technology long ago passed beyond the ken of ordinary mortals. In past ages this didn't matter so much. But now, with the raw energy of the cosmos in the hand of the politician and the soldier, with a new wilderness open for competition among nations armed with this power, and with science thrust into the highest decision-making councils of government, it matters indeed.

Others who provided invaluable research help and criticism include Professor John Foster, Columbia University; Col. William McGinty, Maj. Thomas Ellington and Capt. Russell Turner, United States Air Force; Chris Clausen, Stanley Miller and Ben James, National Aeronautics and Space Administration, and the many companies of the aerospace industry.

A special word of thanks is due Henry Rieger, United Press International, who enabled the author to cover early Space Age developments.

WILLARD E. WILKS

TABLE OF CONTENTS

LIST OF ILLUSTRATIONS

(*between pages 78 and 79*)

xiii

THE NEW WILDERNESS
What We Know About Space

I. THE VOID

What Is Space?

SPACE often is defined merely as "that part of the universe between celestial bodies," leaving the impression that it consists of little more than a vast emptiness worthy of only passing consideration and casual definition. Nothing could be further from the truth, for the fact is that "empty" space contains thinly spread bits of matter that add up to at least as much material as is contained in all the stars. In addition, it is filled with invisible and far-ranging forces and energies, some of which could kill a man exposed to them for only a few minutes.

One theory holds that interstellar space contains, on the average, one atom of matter per pint measure, mostly in the form of gas and dust. The space between galaxies, of course, contains far less.

This may not seem like much; by comparison, a pint of air contains billions of atoms. But space is so immense that all of the stars occupy only a fraction of it. When we consider that the stars are as grains of sand scattered a hundred or more miles apart, we can understand how the billions upon billions of "pints" in between contain a staggering amount of matter.

1

The matter is basically of three kinds: hydrogen gas, dust, and particle radiation.

Hydrogen is the most plentiful, serving as the building-block element for everything from stars to man. It is the simplest of all elements, its atom consisting of one electron whirling around one proton. A theory of how it is built up into other elements through nuclear "cooking" processes in the stars is discussed in the section on evolution of matter.

The exact origin of hydrogen is one of those questions remaining to be answered. One of today's main cosmological theories assumes that it is continually created in space between the galaxies, with no attempt to explain how. The gas is believed to be about one hundred times more plentiful in space than the cosmic dust that is mixed with it.

As for the origin of the dust, one theory is that it condenses from the hydrogen gas. According to calculations by theorists J. H. Oort and H. C. Van de Hulst, it takes about 100,000,000 years for a single dust particle to form from the interstellar gas. Of course, space is so vast that tons of dust would be condensing at any given time. Another theory is that the dust particles are bits of matter ejected from stars.

Interstellar matter is distributed unevenly through our galaxy. In some places, notably the spiral arms, it is gathered into enormous, turbulent clouds that dwarf the solar system. Many of the clouds have fields of stars embedded in them, supporting the idea that stars condense out of such clouds.

Radiation in Space

If we disregard matter, we still find space teeming with radiation, for the stars constantly pour light, heat, and other forms of radiation into surrounding space. The word "radiation" has taken on a mysterious air in the Atomic Age, used as it is to describe phenomena so complicated that few except scientists understand them. Actually, it has the same meaning it always had; it describes anything that radiates from any source, whether matter or energy. Heat radiates from a stove, waves from a dropped stone, and light from a bulb.

There are many kinds of radiation, and most of those found in space also are found, or can be produced, right here on earth. The forms of radiation include light, heat, cosmic rays, X rays, radio and radar waves, and alpha, beta, and gamma rays. They may be divided into two broad categories: electromagnetic radiation and particle radiation.

The first involves radiation of pure energy. It includes light, heat, radio and radar waves, X rays, and gamma rays, all of which travel at the speed of light—186,000 miles per second. The kinds of electromagnetic radiation may be classified according to wave length, and could just as well be labeled 1, 2, 3, etc., instead of with mysterious names.

Particle radiation involves tiny bits of matter, just as the name implies. It includes cosmic rays and alpha and beta rays. The word "rays" is a hangover from the days when science had not yet determined that particles of matter are involved. The particles simply are pieces of atoms shooting through space at terrific velocities, which, in some cases, approach the speed of light. Cosmic-ray particles are believed to be ejected from stars in our galaxy, including the sun.

Specifically, cosmic-ray particles are the nuclei of hydrogen atoms, or protons, although they often include heavier nuclei; beta rays are streams of electrons that have been stripped from atoms, and alpha rays are the nuclei of helium atoms, the second most abundant element.

These tiny bits of matter possess an extraordinary amount of energy because of their high speed. Their concentration of energy per unit of mass may be millions and even billions of times that of artillery shells, depending upon their speed. We are protected from these outer-space projectiles by our blanket of atmosphere, although fragments from their collisions with it sometimes pierce our bodies like tiny bullets.

3

Radiation is, of course, more intense in the vicinity of stars. And within interplanetary space, it is greatly increased from time to time by huge flares, or explosions, on the sun. When these unpredictable flare-ups occur, radiation in interplanetary space is suddenly increased many thousandfold, enough to cause fatal damage to an unprotected man in something like fifteen minutes. The solar outbursts may last for a week or more.

In addition, there are two permanent fields of relatively intense radiation in space near the earth. These fields actually are doughnut-shaped belts surrounding the earth. They are several hundred miles thick over the equatorial area, and thin down to nothing near the polar regions. They are called the Van Allen belts after their discoverer, Dr. James A. Van Allen. One is centered about 2,400 miles from the earth, the other at around 10,000 miles out. The belts are believed caused by the trapping of radioactive particles in the earth's magnetic field.

It appears from the foregoing that so-called empty space is somewhat like a huge shooting gallery with all kinds of radiation flying around in it. Men who go into space must be protected from it, and radiobiologists in the National Aeronautics and Space Administration's space exploration program are devising ways to do this.

Electric and Magnetic Fields

Electricity and magnetism used to be treated as separate things. But as far as modern science can tell, they are virtually inseparable. An electric current is always surrounded by a magnetic field, and a magnetic field often is used to induce an electric current. The two are regarded as stemming from a single force. This force is known as electromagnetism, and it underlies nearly all other forces that involve the interplay of matter, including chemical forces that

4

bind atoms into molecules and cohesive forces that hold larger collections of matter together. Matter, after all, is made of atoms, and atoms consist of electrically charged particles.

Electricity and magnetism together form what is called the electromagnetic field, the medium through which light, heat, radio waves, and all other electromagnetic effects are transmitted across space.

There are electric and magnetic fields throughout the universe. The earth is a magnet, and so is the sun, as well as other stars. The great clouds of hot, turbulent gas in space also generate magnetic fields. Our galaxy as a whole is a magnet. The strength of its field is only a hundred-thousandth that of the earth, but it takes an enormous flow of electric current to maintain such a field across the galaxy's diameter of 100,000 light years.*

Some of the best evidence concerning the existence of electric and magnetic fields in the universe comes from cosmic-ray particles. Many of the particles travel at nearly light speed, making them the fastest known material objects in the universe. Their great speed has long been a puzzle: There are no known nuclear processes that can shoot pieces of matter from atoms with such velocity, and it does not seem possible that ejection from stars could account for it.

How, then, do the particles acquire their great speed?

The answer may have been provided by atom-smashing machines, such as cyclotrons and synchrotrons. These devices push particles to near light speed by giving them many successive kicks with alternating electrical charges as they move in a magnetic field.

Some experts think this process is the only way particles of matter could be made to move so fast, and that nature has

* A light year is the distance light travels in one year—5,880,000,000,000 miles.

its own cosmic-scale synchrotrons in the vast electric and magnetic fields of space.

The length of time some cosmic-ray particles travel in space before reaching the earth tends to confirm this idea. It has been estimated from a study of their chemical composition that some particles have been traveling for 5,300,000 years. This is far longer than they would take if their paths were straight, assuming they originate within our own galaxy. So they must wander through space in devious paths, such as would be the case if they had to pass through chaotic electric and magnetic fields.

Gravity in Space

The term "gravity-free space" has appeared in both popular and scientific literature, implying that there are areas in space where gravity does not exist. But there is no such thing as absolutely gravity-free space. The term is a figure of speech, which, although innocent enough in its intent, can nevertheless lead the layman into needless confusion over some of the most basic facts of space. It is true that under certain conditions men will become "weightless" and float around in a spaceship unless strapped down. But this doesn't mean space travelers will leave the influence of gravity. The condition of weightlessness merely is the result of what scientists call "unrestricted motion in a gravitational field." *

If there is one thing in the universe we cannot avoid, it is gravity. This unseen and mysterious force acts throughout space, binding the planets to the solar system, and stars to galaxies. Its effect reaches over millions of miles of space without being blocked by intervening bodies. For example, when the earth is between the sun and the moon during a lunar eclipse, the moon's motion undergoes no measurable

* See Chapter V.

6

change; the sun's gravitational pull on the moon doesn't appear to be lessened in the least. Although it is dangerous to make flat predictions about science, many experts deem it safe to say that the "antigravity" machine will remain strictly in the realm of science fiction.

In theory, even the gravitational field of the earth, which is relatively weak on the cosmic scale, extends throughout the universe to infinity. It weakens with increasing distance until it becomes negligible, but it never quite ceases. For all practical purposes, though, we can say that an object has "escaped" from the earth when it reaches a point in space where the gravitational influence of another body becomes predominant.

This raises an interesting point which illustrates how easily we may be confused by the pronouncements we see and hear about space: Could we say that a rocket has escaped from the earth when it reaches the moon?

It depends on your point of view. A rocket pilot may feel perfectly justified in answering "yes." But an astronomer, looking at the larger picture, would be technically correct in answering "no," for the moon itself is firmly in the earth's gravitational grasp. We cannot say that a rocket has escaped until it leaves the *earth-moon system* and enters interplanetary space.

From the foregoing discussions, we see that space, far from being empty, contains all of the basic things—materials, energies, forces—that are found anywhere else. Space, it appears, is a sort of tenuous cosmic "soup" which continually receives the prodigious outpourings of all the stars. Our sun alone radiates 4,000,000 tons of matter and energy into space each second.

Nature never is static, and science believes it has discerned a regenerative process going on in space: Many young stars appear to be made from the debris of old ones.

II. MIND OVER SPACE

THEORIES are frustrating substitutes for answers. There are, as yet, no definite answers to what we regard as the most fundamental problems of the universe today: How big is the universe? Is it finite? Is it in an infinite state of expansion? Is it curved? How and when did it start?

Yet, it is a measure of the power of theory and of scientific progress that only a few hundred years ago the most pressing questions of cosmology were: Is the earth flat or round? Does it move? Is it the center of the universe? Is the sun a star?

Every child knows the answers to these questions today before he is ten years old. But it required six thousand years of torturously acquired knowledge to enable us to take for granted a few simple conclusions, such as:

The Earth Is a Sphere—This theory was proposed as early as the sixth century B.C. by Greek astronomer-philosopher Anaximander. He observed that while the Big Dipper always remains above the horizon in Greece, it dips below the horizon for a time each night in Egypt. He reasoned from this that the earth could not be a flat disc, for if it were, the Dipper should appear equally high above the horizon everywhere on earth. Anaximander also concluded that the dome of heaven must be spherical, extending completely around the earth, underneath as well as above.

This was a breakthrough of antiquity. The earth became a body floating freely in three-dimensional space, and man's idea of the universe had to be enlarged considerably. But Greek cosmology never got beyond that, not even with the great Aristotle, who in the fourth century B.C. defined the concepts that dominated man's thought for the next two thousand years. The earth remained fixed, an immovable sphere in the center of the universe with everything else revolving around it. Of course, this remained pure theory so far as the common man was concerned, so the idea that the earth was a flat plane stayed widespread for centuries.

The Earth Is a Planet—The Greek idea, of course, was wholly inadequate for explaining the observed motions of the solar system, and this became more apparent as the science of astronomy progressed. Astronomers, in order to fit the movements of the "wandering stars"—other planets—to this model, were driven to inventing a series of circles or orbits for each body, and it seemed as if they never could find the right number or combination of circles.

By the time of Nicolaus Copernicus (1473-1543), astronomers had constructed a fantastic system of 10,000 celestial circles to explain how things operated in the heavens. Copernicus, as he put it, simply couldn't believe that the Creator Himself would need that many circles. He proposed a magnificent simplification: the sun, not the earth, as the center of the universe, and the earth merely another planet. Only one orbit was needed for each body.

The Copernican theory required another great revision in man's idea of the size of the universe. For if the earth plied a huge orbit around the sun, then the stars must be an unimaginable distance away—otherwise, there would be con-

9

siderable changes in their positions in the sky as the earth moved around the sun.

The Sun Is a Star—Copernicus' views were so radical for their time that the calculations and drawings he offered were rejected. But he had followers. One of them, the Italian philosopher Giordano Bruno (1548?-1600), even went a step further and proposed that the sun was just another star among countless stars in an infinite cosmos. Banishing the earth from the center of the universe was bad enough; doing the same to the sun was unforgivable heresy, and Bruno was burned at the stake for his vision.

The Binding Force—By the seventeenth century, following discovery that the orbital velocities of the planets diminish with distance from the sun—Mercury travels faster than Venus, etc.—scientists had begun to conceive that some physical force was needed to bind things together in the solar system. Why should the planets revolve eternally around the sun? Why should they circle at different speeds, depending upon their distance from the sun? The sun must exert a force on them, an attractive force which decreases with distance.

Out of this evolved the theory of mutual attraction of all bodies in the universe. The earth attracted objects so that they fell; perhaps the sun attracted the earth in the same way. The earth must constantly try to move in two directions at once—toward the sun and straight out into space. The result is that it does neither, but continues "falling" in an eternal curve around its attracting body.

Sir Isaac Newton (1642-1727) put all this into a simple mathematical formula called the Universal Law of Gravitation:

$$\text{Gravitation} = \frac{\text{product of the masses}}{\text{square of the distance}}$$

The formula states that the force of attraction between any pair of bodies is equal to the product of their masses divided by the square of their distance apart.

This became the fundamental formula of astronomy, applying to any body in the universe, even to the smallest particle of matter. With it astronomers actually could "weigh" the stars. And its application to tiny deviations in the orbits of known planets resulted in predictions of planets and moons as yet undiscovered by telescopes.

The Stars Are Moving—One of the momentous conclusions which Newton's Law of Gravitation made inevitable was that everything in space must be in constant motion, otherwise the force of gravity would pile all matter into one huge mass. If, for instance, the planets were stopped in their orbits, they would fall into the sun.

In 1718, Edmund Halley, an astronomer friend of Newton, checked stellar positions plotted by the Greeks two thousand years before and noted changes which showed that the stars are in motion. Man had stared at the seemingly unchanging constellations for thousands of years and thought the stars were fixed. Actually, they are traveling helter-skelter in space like the dust particles visible in a beam of light. They are moving in all directions at speeds of hundreds of miles per second. But they are so far away that while they may move a million miles in space, it appears they haven't moved even a fraction of a degree.

We Live in a Galaxy—Our galaxy was "discovered" around 1740 by Thomas Wright, an English instrument maker. It took no special instruments for Wright to make the discovery. He merely stared at the stars as had countless observers before him, but he saw what others had not, and was struck with an idea that gave man a revolutionary new picture of the universe.

Up to that time it had been assumed that the misty band of light we call the Milky Way was simply a section of sky where distant stars were collected thicker than elsewhere. But Wright asked: Are the stars really thicker there, or does it just *appear* that way because there are more layers of stars stretching into space in that direction? He theorized that we are inside a wheel-shaped system of stars and that the Milky Way is what we see when we look toward the rim.

Thirteen years later, Immanuel Kant extended this idea an important step further. He concluded that the faint elliptical objects discerned among the stars by telescopes of those days were in reality other galaxies.

These discoveries enabled science for the first time to draw what seemed a fairly complete picture of the universe. Its structure was revealed from the solar system to the galaxy to other stellar systems. And the binding force of all this had been found and set to a powerful formula, Newton's Law of Gravitation; man at last could accurately trace and predict movements in the heavens. The universe was seen as a sort of cosmic clockwork in which the planets, moons, stars, and galaxies wheeled in precise obedience to Newton's law.

Modern Cosmology

The Newtonian, or classical, concept of the universe demanded that we think of it as consisting of bits and chunks of matter scattered over a vast area with little or nothing in between except an invisible something designated "ether." Today, largely due to the theories of Albert Einstein, we regard that idea as a mechanical model that falls far short of explaining the nature of the universe.

Modern cosmology presents the stuff of the universe as consisting of a single primordial medium that is spread thick in some places and thin in others. What is this medium to which everything has been reduced? Energy. An atom, a man, a planet, or a star simply is concentrated or congealed energy.

The space between the congealed lumps contains thinly spread energy in other forms such as described in Chapter I.

The equivalence of matter and energy was deduced from Einstein's principle of the *relativity of mass,* as stated in his Special Theory of Relativity. In classical physics, the mass of a body is something that is incapable of change; it remains the same whether an object is at rest or speeding through space at millions of miles an hour. But Einstein's equations showed that mass is relative—it increases with motion. The increase is too small to be noticed at ordinary velocities. But at speeds approaching that of light it becomes enormous. This is borne out in the laboratory when nuclear particles are shot to speeds near that of light in atom-smashing machines —the mass of a particle actually increases with motion. Atom smashers, in fact, must be built to take this into account.

Einstein drew a simple but momentous conclusion from his theory. He reasoned that since motion is a form of energy—kinetic energy—the increased mass of a moving object is a result of its increased energy. Energy, therefore, has mass; it is equivalent to matter. Matter and energy are simply different states of the same thing.

Einstein's idea is expressed in the equation $E = mc^2$, which states that the total energy contained in any body of matter is equal to the mass of the body multiplied by the square of the velocity of light.

The speed of light is a very large number—186,000 miles per second—and when we take the mass of any body of matter and multiply it by the square of this number we can see that matter represents a staggering amount of concentrated energy. A mere pound of coal, if converted *entirely* to energy, would produce more than enough power to drive a battleship around the world. The ordinary burning of coal is a purely chemical process which releases far less than a billionth of its total energy.

The Atomic Age was born with publication of this equation in 1905, although it wasn't until forty years later that its simple premise resulted in detonation of the first atomic bomb.

To the cosmologist, the formula's greatest significance lay in its ability to solve ages-old secrets of the universe, such as where the sun and stars obtain the energy necessary to keep them radiating light and heat for eons.

The equivalence of matter and energy makes it somewhat easier to accept some of the other startling things predicted by Einstein's theory, such as the contraction of moving bodies and the slowdown of time.

Einstein's ideas grew out of conclusions he drew from an experiment conducted in 1881 by two American physicists, A. A. Michelson and E. W. Morley. The experiment was performed to prove or disprove the existence of ether.

The ether fitted nicely with the Newtonian idea that space itself could somehow be used as a fixed frame of reference—a sort of background—against which the movements of all celestial bodies could be detected and measured. The ether was believed to be the one stationary thing in the universe, though no one actually had been able to prove this, or even that ether existed.

Michelson and Morley reasoned that if light is propagated through the ether, its speed should be affected by the "ether wind" resulting from the earth's movement through the fixed medium. The earth travels around the sun at 18½ miles per second. So a beam of light projected in the direction of the earth's movement—*against* the wind—should be retarded by 18½ miles per second, and a beam sent *with* the wind should be speeded by the same amount.

The two scientists set up their experiment on a solid stone

table. Since it was impossible to measure the speed of a light beam over a short distance, they used a unique method to detect any change in velocity. The beams were projected from a source at right angles to each other, one traveling against the ether stream, the other across it. They traveled equal distances and then were reflected back over their courses to an instrument which could tell whether they arrived at the same instant.

The experiment was conducted many times, with the apparatus turned in all directions, and the puzzling result was that absolutely no difference was detected in the speed of the beams.

This confronted science with a serious dilemma. Of course, it could be explained by simply giving up the ether theory, but that meant throwing away other theories that had worked for years. Various explanations that would allow science to keep its cherished ether were put forward. One, proposed by Irish scientist G. F. FitzGerald in 1893, was very simple: All objects flatten on impact with solid surfaces, so why shouldn't they be contracted a bit by the impact of the ether wind?

Michelson and Morley had projected their light beams over equal distances marked on the stone table. But, Fitz-Gerald said, the courses only *appeared* equal; the one turned in the direction of the earth's movement actually had been shortened by contraction of the stone table just enough to equalize the speed of the beams. In other words, a beam sent in that direction had a shorter distance to cover, compensating for its slowing by the ether wind. Of course, no ordinary measuring rod could detect this because it, too, would be shortened by exactly the same amount when laid along that direction.

FitzGerald's argument appealed to many scientists who were reluctant to give up the ether theory. It is not unusual for science to entertain ideas which seem to defy common sense. The primary consideration is, do they work?

Two years later, a Dutch physicist, H. A. Lorentz, lent support to the contraction hypothesis with his electron theory of the composition of matter. Lorentz theorized that matter is composed of electrical charges, and when these move through the electric and magnetic fields residing in the ether, they are changed and caused to move, resulting in contraction.

Starting with the Michelson-Morley experiment, Einstein drew two postulates:

- The ether cannot be detected.
- The velocity of light is unaffected by the motion of the earth.

At first glance, these two plain statements may seem to border on the trivial, merely pointing out the obvious. But Einstein used them as the basis for a revolutionary line of reasoning.

The ether cannot be detected—If this is so, we must give up the idea of a stationary, absolute frame of reference against which all motion in the universe can be detected. Now, what do we have left with which to detect and measure the motion of a body? Only other bodies. It's not difficult to see that if the earth suddenly were left alone in space, we would have no means of telling whether we were at rest or hurtling along at millions of miles an hour; there would be no guideposts, no background of "scenery" against which we could detect our motion. Thus, the movement of any body in space can be measured only in relation to some other body.

The velocity of light is unaffected by the motion of the earth—In other words, it is always *constant* relative to an observer regardless of the observer's motion in space. Since it is illogical to think that this behavior of light should be restricted to our little portion of the universe, it must be a rule of nature throughout the cosmos. The speed of light must be a universal constant. It's not too much of a jump from this to the conclusion that the velocity of light must be the top limiting speed in the universe—nothing can move faster.

What Einstein says is that regardless of an observer's speed or direction, he will always measure the velocity of light as 186,000 miles a second. This seems contrary to common sense, although it is scientific fact. If we drive an automobile at fifty miles an hour into a wind of twenty miles an hour, we measure the wind's approach as seventy miles an hour. But this rule of addition of velocities doesn't hold where light is concerned. An automobile driven into a stream of light will always register its approach as 186,000 miles per second, even if the vehicle itself reaches light speed.

How can this be? Does light somehow adjust itself to a moving object so that it always meets the object at the same speed? Or does something happen to the object? Something has to give.

The Special Theory says that since the speed of light is constant, an object's time and dimension must vary. Einstein found a means of doing this in the Lorentz-FitzGerald contraction, although rejecting the original reason for its proposal.

Let us use a rocket ship shooting through space as an example. The theory holds that in order for the velocity of light to remain unchanged in relation to the rocket, the vehicle's measuring devices must contract and its clocks slow down. The rocket and everything in it must contract along its line of motion. And the closer the ship approaches light speed, the greater the contraction and time slowdown. If the rocket could reach light speed, the theory predicts it would shrink to nothing, becoming energy. However, this is held to be impossible because it would take an infinite amount of energy to propel any object that fast, and there just isn't that much energy in the universe.

The theory also says that persons riding in the rocket wouldn't be able to notice their own contraction and time slowdown because all things, regardless of their composition, contract by the same amount, and all physical processes, including those of a living organism, slow down together. However, if an observer in space could get a close look at the rocket as it sped by, it would appear that it was shorter and its clocks running slower.

In our world of relatively slow speeds, contraction and time slowdown are too small to be measured. An object's length is cut in half and its mass doubled when its speed reaches 161,000 miles a second. After that, length and mass change rapidly toward zero and infinity, and time nears a standstill.

This is all very difficult to imagine, and discussion of it may seem artificial. After all, we cannot go out into space and measure a rocket shooting by at millions of miles an hour. But Einstein's predictions have been verified in several ways. The time slowdown has been shown in the laboratory. When the frequency of vibration of atoms moving at high speed is compared with that of slow-moving atoms, the vibration of the former is slowed exactly as the equations predict.

Why is the frequency of vibration slowed? This has been explained as due to an increase in the inertia, or mass, of the atom. The atom cannot vibrate as fast as it did before because an increase in its inertia is an increase in its tendency to resist motion.

Time is not a quantity that exists of itself. It is simply a series of events; it does not exist unless marked in some

18

way. The vibrations of atoms are a series of events, and when they are slowed, time is slowed.

Einstein's equations do not explain the actual mechanisms by which these phenomena occur. But it may become easier to accept them if we reconsider the principle of equivalence of matter and energy: If matter is energy, what is so odd about it changing its dimension and rate of vibration when it shoots through the universe at high speed?

Einstein's upsetting of the classical concepts didn't stop there. He next turned his attention to gravity and how it determines the structure and size of the universe.

The effects of gravity have been defined so precisely by mathematical formulas that the positions of the planets can be predicted for millions of years in the future. But despite this, science today can no more state exactly what gravity is or what causes it than ancient man could explain the wind. For this reason, modern science uses two theories of gravity. The theories, developed by Newton and Einstein, give fundamentally different explanations of the cause of gravity.

Newton explains gravity as a force of attraction existing among all bodies of matter in the universe, from atoms to stars. In his view, one body goes around another, such as the earth around the sun, because the two exert a pull on each other.

Einstein's General Theory of Relativity states, on the other hand, that the earth goes around the sun because space is *built*, or curved, that way in the vicinity of the sun. However, his theory doesn't necessarily prove that Newton is wrong. To this day, astronomy finds Newton's law generally adequate to explain the movements of bodies in the universe. But in a number of important instances, it has been found that Einstein's theory comes closer to the truth.

Einstein developed his theory out of certain objections to Newton's ideas. One of his main objections centered around a curious phenomenon of gravity—the fact that all bodies fall at the same rate, regardless of their weight, size, or composition.

A pebble and an automobile dropped from a building together will fall at exactly the same rate and hit the ground at the same instant (neglecting the difference in air resistance). This seems to defy one of Newton's own laws of motion, which says that the force required to move a body is directly proportional to the mass of the body and that an equal force applied to bodies of different masses will cause greater movement in the smaller body.

This law works fine for bodies in horizontal motion. But it doesn't seem to apply when bodies are falling under the influence of gravity, for they invariably fall at exactly the same rate.

Newton explained this in his theory by assuming that gravity somehow is able to automatically adjust its pull to fit the mass, or inertia, of the body it attracts; the heavier the object, the stronger the pull, the lighter the object, the weaker the pull.

Einstein couldn't accept this explanation. He rejected Newton's idea of "action at a distance." He refused to believe that one body could reach out across millions of miles and exert an instantaneous physical force on another—a force always adjusted to the exact amount needed. In his words:

"We have come to regard action at a distance as a process impossible without the intervention of some intermediate medium. If, for instance, a magnet attracts a piece of iron, we cannot be content to regard this as meaning that the magnet acts *directly* on the iron through the intermediate empty space, but we are constrained to imagine . . . that the magnet always calls into being *something physically real* in the space around it, that something being what we call a 'magnetic field.' In its turn, this magnetic field operates on

20

the piece of iron, so that the latter strives to move towards the magnet." *

Einstein, of course, does not mean to say that a gravitational field is the same as a magnetic field. But he notes the similarities among gravitational, magnetic, and electric fields.

In Einstein's view, then, a body of matter creates something physically real in the space around it, a field of what often is called distortion or curvature. The structure of the field can be seen in the distribution of the planets around the sun, just as iron filings scattered around a magnet reveal the structure of the magnetic field.

The field of gravity around a body extends out in all directions, weakening with distance, but theoretically extending throughout space. Thus, the fields produced by all bodies of matter in the universe add up to an overall structure or *medium*. Space is seen as a plastic medium that is shaped by the presence and motion of the bodies embedded in it.

Just what originally set the celestial bodies in motion through space is of no concern in Einstein's theory. It attempts only to describe and define what is observed. It does this through groups of laws that deal with the relationship between the mass of a body and the structure of its gravitational field, and which describe movements of bodies under the influence of gravity.

Einstein concluded that space wasn't empty, but contained a medium, just as the classical physicists had thought. However, the ether medium of Newtonian physics was merely an inert, stationary something invented to transmit electromagnetic phenomena, and space was treated as empty for all practical purposes beyond that.

The theories of Newton and Einstein, although they differ fundamentally, produce very nearly the same answers to

* Albert Einstein, *Relativity, the Special and General Theory,* trans. by Robert W. Lawson (New York: Bonanza Book, Crown Publishers, Inc., n.d.), p. 74. The italics are the author's.

most astronomical problems. In fact, there usually is no point in bothering with Einstein's more complicated concepts. But there are some exceptional problems of astronomy which can be solved only with Einstein's theory. One of these has to do with the effect of a gravitational field upon light. Classical physics holds that light always travels in a straight line. Einstein's theory, however, holds that since light is energy—and, therefore, has mass—it must be affected by gravity, that it is curved when passing through a strong gravitational field. Einstein suggested that this could be shown by photographing a star appearing just at the edge of the sun's disc during the darkness of a total eclipse and comparing it with a picture of the same star made some other time. When such photographs are compared, the position of the star appears to have shifted very slightly when it is seen near the sun's disc, confirming that a light ray from the star is curved in toward the sun in traveling from the star to earth.

The theories of Newton and Einstein also produce different answers concerning the shape and size of the universe. Newton concluded that all matter was concentrated at the center of the universe, with an infinite void extending beyond that.

Einstein presents quite a different view: The distortions created by all bodies in the universe have a total effect—they add up to a total, overall curvature. Space, like a drop of water, curves back on itself to form a finite, spherical universe.

This universe is said to be *finite* but *unbounded*. How can there be such a thing? Scientists usually explain it this way: It is the four-dimensional counterpart of the surface of a sphere. It curves back on itself, and if a person traveled long enough in any direction, he eventually would wind up where he started.

The two theories also differ interestingly on the probable

fate of the universe. In Newton's model, there would be a constant escape of light, heat, and all other radiant energy into the infinite void. The universe eventually would dissipate its energy, grow cold, and die. Einstein's model, on the other hand, presents a universe that could go on forever. If space curves back on itself, energy never can escape. Perhaps it collects into new stars and galaxies somewhere. If so, the universe never will die.

While Einstein's gravitational law seems in some ways to present a more accurate picture of the universe than Newton's, science continues to use both theories. Sometimes gravity is treated as a force of attraction, at other times as a curvature of space, depending upon which explanation seems to best fit a given situation. If this seems inconsistent, it is, and we should learn to expect it. After all, neither theory really explains what gravity is. Both start with the observed motion of bodies in the universe, and from there seek to develop a consistent set of rules to describe and predict these motions.

The Expanding Universe

It is curious that an error in one of Einstein's calculations provided the tip-off to the next big revolution in cosmology —the discovery that the universe is expanding. The error was in Einstein's proof for a static universe, one which may change internally but not as a whole. The mistake was discovered in 1922 by a Russian mathematician, Alexander A. Friedman, who proceeded to work out mathematically two possible nonstatic models of the universe—one expanding, the other contracting.

This does not mean that Einstein's other conclusions are invalid; relativity remains the basis for all theoretical models of the universe.

At the time Friedman made his calculations, astronomers

had begun to notice a general shift in the light from the distant galaxies toward the red end of the spectrum. The "red shift" was identified as the well-known Doppler effect, which is the lengthening of wavelengths of light or sound from a source that is moving rapidly away from an observer.

An American astronomer, Edwin P. Hubble of the Mount Wilson Observatory in California, undertook a study of the red shift, and in 1929 announced his conclusion: The universe is in a state of expansion, with all of the galaxies rushing away from us and each other at incredible speeds.

Hubble found that the nearer galaxies are receding at several million miles an hour. The expansion process is such that the farther from us a galaxy is, the faster it is traveling away; every time the distance doubles, the speed of recession also is approximately doubled. (Plate 1.)

The most distant galaxies discovered to date with the world's largest optical telescope—the 200-inch instrument at Mount Palomar, California—are in a cluster located in the constellation of Boötes. The cluster is about four billion light years from us. It is estimated to be rushing away at more than 300,000,000 miles an hour, nearly half the speed of light. (Plate 2.)

The Mount Palomar telescope has a range over an area of space believed to contain at least one billion galaxies. Those galaxies near the limit of observation are so faint that they cannot be seen directly; they must be detected by photographic means, and become visible as tiny specks on a plate only after long exposure.

It is at this extreme limit that the answers to the major problems of cosmology are being sought today. Astronomers want to know: Are the galaxies beginning to slow down? Are they more thickly distributed in distant space? Are collisions between galaxies more frequent there?

The answers to these questions may show which of our current theoretical models of the universe is correct.

24

Evolutionary vs. Steady-State Universe

There are two major theories as to the nature and origin of the universe. Both assume that the universe is in a state of expansion.

One theory accounts for the expansion by supposing that it is the result of a titanic explosion, or at least a sudden expansion of great force, that began billions of years ago. At the beginning, it proposes, all matter was concentrated into a colossal lump or cloud of nuclear material. This superdense primeval atom was unstable, and when it disintegrated it sent pieces flying out in all directions. The chunks have been traveling ever since, cooling and forming into stars and galaxies.

This often is called the "big bang" theory. More scientifically, it is known as the "evolutionary" theory, since it holds that the universe is evolving, that is, changing with time. Specifically, it states that the galaxies are drawing *farther apart from each other* as they fly outward. This is an important point for determining which of the theoretical models is correct. It means that the number of galaxies in any given volume of space must decrease with the passing eons.

The other theory accounts for the expansion by proposing that matter is being created spontaneously and continually in space between the galaxies. The outward pressure resulting from this never-ending flow of new matter pushes everything apart, and new galaxies form from the new matter at a rate which just compensates for the expansion. This idea is called the "steady state" theory, for it holds that instead of changing with time, the number of galaxies in any given volume of space remains forever the same.

Answers to such questions as "When and how did the universe start?"; "How big is it?"; "Is it in an infinite state of expansion?" must be sought in these two theories, for they are the only ones under serious consideration today.

If the evolutionary theory is right, the "age" of the universe, as figured from the time of the explosion, is about eight billion years. What happened and how much time elapsed before that is anybody's guess. As for size, the theory says the universe may be finite or infinite—it depends on whether expansion goes on forever or eventually stops.

If the steady-state theory is correct, the universe has no beginning or end in terms of time or size; matter is continually created throughout the cosmos and spreads into infinite space. Where does the matter come from? The theory doesn't try to answer that; it simply states that creation of matter must be occurring in order for the theory to work. According to proponents of this idea, the rate at which matter appears is about one atom of hydrogen in a volume of space the size of a twenty- or thirty-story building per year.

The main task of cosmologists is to determine which of these theories may be correct by subjecting them to certain observational tests. In making these tests, science receives a lucky break in at least one respect: Looking out into the depths of space is exactly like looking into a science-fiction time machine which shows us the past. The farther we look into space, the farther we look back in time. We see the nearest star, Alpha Centauri, as it was four and a half years ago, the nearest galaxy, Andromeda, as it looked 2,300,000 years ago, and the most distant galaxies as they were about four billion years ago. Thus, we can study the history of the universe by direct observation.

One of the most obvious tests is to see if there has been a change in the population density of galaxies over the past few billion years. If the density increases with distance from us—that is, if galaxies appear thicker in number—it would indicate all galaxies were once much closer together and that we live in an evolutionary universe. If, on the other hand, we find the distribution of galaxies to be the same no matter how far we look into space—and back in time—the steady-state theory would be supported.

Evidence so far seems to favor the evolutionary theory, although it is by no means conclusive. Until recently, substantial support for the evolutionary idea was believed to have been provided by radio telescopes, which can probe much farther into space than optical instruments by listening to radio "noise" emitted by some galaxies and clusters of galaxies. An interpretation of the radio telescope data was that an increasing density of galaxies had been detected with increasing distance.

This interpretation very conveniently tied in with the startling discovery of what appeared to be colliding galaxies in distant space. (Plate 3.) For if galaxies appear thicker in number in distant space (*appear,* because remember that we are seeing them as they *were* eons ago), we should expect to see more collisions there than in nearer space.

More recent observational evidence has challenged interpretation of the radio telescope data, however. The newer evidence is based on the discovery that awesome explosions apparently have occurred in the centers of some galaxies where stars and gas have massed into an enormous nucleus or superstar. What in some cases had seemed to be pairs of colliding galaxies now appear to be single ones, the centers of which have blown vast clouds of hot gas into nearby space. Since such gas can produce intense radio noise, these galaxies could account for some of the extremely strong sources of radio noise detected in the far reaches of space.

This new development does not necessarily rule out collisions between galaxies. According to estimates by astronomers, collisions of galaxies are far more likely than collisions of stars because the stars are spread much farther apart in relation to their size than are galaxies. In fact, it is held likely that galaxies in collision pass through each other without collisions of their stars. We are assured by some experts that neither a collision with another galaxy nor an explosion of the nucleus of our own galaxy would necessarily harm our planet.

Still another test of the two theories involves measuring the speed of expansion at different times in the history of the universe. If there was an explosion, the pieces were moving outward much faster at the beginning—they have been slowing down ever since due to the opposing pull of gravity exerted by all of the matter in the universe.

We have noted that the farther we look into space, the faster the galaxies appear to be moving away, and that their speed increases in direct proportion to their distance. Now, if the explosion theory is correct, we should find that the more distant galaxies appear to be receding *faster* than in direct proportion to distance. Astronomers at the Mount Palomar Observatory believe they have found such galaxies starting at about one billion light years from us.

The evolutionary theory proposes two possible models for the universe, the "hyperbolic" and the "pulsating."

In the first, expansion is unlimited; the fleeing galaxies will be slowed by the force of gravity, but never enough to stop expansion.

In the pulsating model, expansion is limited. The braking effect of gravity eventually will halt expansion and the universe will begin to contract. It will take as many billions of years for the galaxies to be drawn back together as it took for them to reach their ultimate state of dispersion. The return to the superdense lump will last for only an instant, for the concentration of energies resulting from the big squeeze will cause another explosion, a rebirth, as it were. The cycle of oscillation might be on the order of eighty billion years.

Which of these models fits our universe? Evidence so far is inconclusive. On one hand, measurements of distant galaxies indicate that the rate of expansion may be slowing enough to favor the pulsating model. On the other, there is evidence that the rate of expansion is far more than enough to overcome the opposing force of gravity.

How may we determine which of these models is correct?

The expansion of the universe may be likened to what happens when a rocket is fired into space from the earth. If the rocket is shot at less than the velocity of escape from earth—25,000 miles an hour—it can travel only so far before gravity gradually brings it to a stop and starts pulling it back. But if the rocket is launched at escape velocity or better, it will continue moving away from the earth forever, even though slowed considerably by gravity.

The speed required to escape from any given body depends upon that body's mass. The more massive the body, the higher the speed necessary.

Similarly, the velocity required for the galaxies to escape forever from each other—resulting in unlimited expansion—depends upon how much matter the universe contains. Current observational estimates are that if the material in the galaxies were spread evenly through space, the density of matter in the universe would be about one hydrogen atom per 1,000 "quarts" of space. If this figure is correct, the observed speed of galactic recession is several times that necessary for unlimited expansion to occur.

But we are by no means certain this density figure is right. In the first place, estimates as to the amount of material in the galaxies themselves could be far off the mark. In the second place, there may be a great deal of pure hydrogen gas in space that cannot be detected at present.

There is, in fact, evidence that something is quite wrong with the density estimate. As we noted earlier, measurements with the 200-inch telescope indicate that the rate of expansion may be slowing enough for gravity to gain the upper hand. According to Allan Sandage of the Mount Palomar Observatory, the rate of slowdown calls for a density of

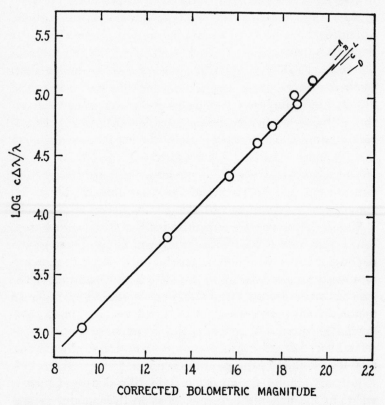

Figure 1. Our expanding universe as it is being charted by Mount Palomar astronomers, plotting speed and distance of receding galaxies. Which way the line bends as more galaxies are plotted on the chart in the next few years will indicate which theoretical model of the universe is correct. (Courtesy Dr. W. A. Baum, Mount Palomar Observatory.)

about 200 times the current estimate. So the issue is in a great deal of doubt.

Astronomers think that within the next few years they might be able to determine which model our universe fits by use of the plot shown in Figure 1.

The points distributed along the line on the chart represent eight clusters of galaxies observed by Mount Palomar. The last cluster plotted, at the top end of the line, is the most distant and fastest receding cluster observed to date. The red shift of these clusters has been plotted against their apparent magnitude, or crudely stated, their speed of recession against their distance. The line, or curve, drawn through the points should, after several times as many clusters have been plotted, indicate which theoretical model our universe fits. The small lines drawn at the upper end of the curve indicate directions in which the curve might bend as more clusters are plotted. Lines A, B, and C all represent an exploding universe (exploding at different speeds), and line D is where the curve eventually would bend if we live in a steady-state universe. Line L is the dividing line between an exploding universe that eventually collapses (limited expansion) and an exploding universe that will not collapse (unlimited expansion).

Thus, if the curve remains above L as more clusters are plotted, the chart will indicate that our universe will collapse sometime in the far future, while bending below L will mean unending expansion. The curve plotted so far points toward a collapse. However, Dr. W. A. Baum, who provided the chart, cautions that the data are very preliminary and that future correction could change the chart somewhat.

If the universe is finite, how big is it? As we have seen, there are so many uncertainties involved that any definite figure is to be regarded with suspicion. But for those interested in some kind of figure, an estimate of fifteen to twenty billion light years for the radius of the universe is as good as any.

III. SPACESHIP EARTH

MEN going into space will set some impressive speed records, but they will have to go some to better the speeds at which mankind already is hurtling through the universe.

The earth is taking us on a journey that, for speed and distance traveled, will be difficult for man-made vehicles to match. It whirls around the sun at a speed of 66,600 miles an hour, daily covering more than 1,500,000 miles along its 580,000,000-mile orbit. The solar system, in turn, moves in a huge orbit about the galactic hub at a speed of 720,000 miles an hour, plunging through space more than 17,000,000 miles every day.

While this is going on, the galaxy moves with respect to neighboring galaxies at some 360,000 miles per hour. But this is barely getting around. Our galactic speed with respect to the most distant galaxies recognized to date is about 300,000,000 miles an hour, nearly half the speed of light. And some theorists hold that our speed relative to the furthermost galaxies, which our instruments haven't yet been able to detect, may approach the speed of light.

We may draw various awesome comparisons in which the earth is likened to a pea, a grain of sand, or a dust mote in relation to the solar system, the galaxy, and the rest of the cosmos. But we really do not need such comparisons when the facts speak eloquently for themselves.

Consider the earth's path around the sun. It deviates from a straight line by only one-ninth of an *inch* in 18½ miles, the distance the planet travels along its orbit in one second. This is so nearly straight that for all surveying purposes on earth it is considered perfect. Think how many such lines a surveyor would have to draw in order to bring the earth full circle around the sun—31,536,000, the number of seconds in a year.

We have noted that the solar system travels 17,000,000 miles in its galactic orbit each day. In a year's time, this adds up to more than six billion miles. But the galaxy is so immense that the solar system takes more than 200,000,000 years to make one circuit. Spaceship earth has covered but a few "days'" journey around the galaxy since the beginning of mankind.

Composition and Structure

Daily in the course of our travels within the solar system, we run into clouds of dust, meteoritic particles no larger than a grain of sand, and big chunks of rock and metal. We are protected from this cosmic debris by our shell of atmosphere which extends up to 1,000 miles or more from the earth's surface. Most of the objects encountered are consumed in the terrific heat of friction generated when they slam into the atmosphere. But many are small enough to slip through the air without burning up, and others are so large they are not completely consumed before reaching the earth's surface. As a result, there is a steady rain of ashes and particles to earth from space, and it is estimated the earth is getting fatter by perhaps as much as 1,000,000 tons per day.

In addition to acting as a meteor bumper during our

travels through space, the atmosphere screens out harmful radiation and distributes light and heat evenly over the planet's surface. The moon is the same distance from the sun, but, lacking an atmosphere, its surface is exposed directly to both the glare of the sun and the cold of outer space, with temperatures ranging from 214 degrees F. down to −250 degrees F.

Ordinarily we do not think of our atmosphere as being very dense. It is not insofar as planetary atmospheres go, but it is up to 1,000 times denser than the material in some stars, the so-called red giants. Betelgeuse, second brightest star in the Orion constellation, is one such star. Astronomers call Betelgeuse, which is 24,000,000 times as voluminous as the sun, a "red-hot vacuum."

The earth's atmosphere is unique among the planets in that it contains relatively large amounts of free oxygen, necessary for animal life as we know it, and water vapor. The air is composed of about 78 per cent nitrogen and 21 per cent oxygen, with argon, carbon dioxide, hydrogen, and other gases making up the remaining one per cent. In contrast, little or no free oxygen and water vapor have been detected in the atmospheres of other planets.

Man has learned relatively little firsthand information about the earth's internal structure, never having penetrated far into the outer crust, which is twenty to thirty miles thick. However, much has been inferred from the study of how earthquake waves are bent as they travel through the globe. This research shows that the earth is composed of concentric shells of varying composition and density. Each affects seismic waves in a different way. Half a dozen or more shells have been recognized in seismic studies, but, in general, the earth consists of two parts, a molten nickel-iron core 4,000 miles in diameter and an outer solid covering of stony material—the mantle—which makes up the rest of the earth's 7,970-mile diameter. The crust is the outer skin of the mantle. The most abundant elements of the crust include oxygen and silicon, which make up about 75 per cent of the total, and aluminum, iron, calcium, sodium, potassium, and magnesium. Age of the earth, as determined by measurement of radioactivity in its rocks, is four to six billion years.

The earth's composition and construction give it both great rigidity and elasticity. If it could be dropped onto a huge concrete slab, it would not shatter, as one might think, but would bounce better than a steel ball bearing. The earth's elasticity is shown by the tides that the gravitational pull of the moon and sun raise on its solid surface. During the time of greatest tidal pull—when the moon and sun are lined up on one side of the earth—our planet's crust bulges up about nine inches. As the earth turns, this bulge is dragged across the crust like a swell in water. If the earth were a totally rigid body it would be cracked and split by this action.

The theory that the earth's core is liquid is based in part on the fact that it has a magnetic field. Although science cannot say definitely, the magnetic field is believed to be the result of the earth's rotation and electric currents produced by the stirring of a molten interior. The field constantly fluctuates in strength and direction over the earth's surface.

Strength of the field actually is much less than that of a toy magnet. Yet the earth's magnetic history has been frozen into its rocks. When lava flows out on the surface, it carries magnetic mineral grains which become magnetized in the direction of the field at that particular location. After the lava solidifies, these tiny magnets remain as permanent records unaffected by future geomagnetic changes.

Investigation of layer upon layer of lava flows in some parts of the world has revealed the puzzling fact that the earth's magnetic poles have reversed places several times. This has suggested to some researchers that the planet's

35

axis of rotation must have changed—that the earth has flip-flopped in space.

Double Planet

One of the earth's most unusual features is the size of its moon. Our satellite is sixth in size among the planets' thirty-one moons, but it is the biggest in comparison to its parent body. Its 2,160-mile diameter is more than a quarter of the earth's. It is proper to consider the earth-moon system a double planet.

Other satellites are tiny compared to their planets. Saturn, for example, has the largest moon, Titan, whose 3,500-mile diameter is 400 miles greater than that of the smallest planet, Mercury. But Saturn's diameter is more than twenty times that of Titan's. Two of Jupiter's twelve moons also are giants, with diameters of 3,200 miles. But again they are tiny alongside Jupiter's 88,000-mile breadth.

The moon's size has led to speculation that it is another planet captured during a close approach to earth. Most satellites move in orbits which lie around the planets' equators. But our moon's path is tilted from the equator, lying in a plane almost parallel to the plane of the earth's orbit. This indicates, perhaps, that the moon once traveled its own path around the sun.

The Sun's Family

Before considering the earth's possible origin, take a look at the rest of the solar system. The sun's family is composed of nine known planets, thirty-one moons, 30,000 or more "minor planets," or asteroids, most of them lying in a belt between Mars and Jupiter; about 100 billion comets, uncounted meteoroids, and great quantities of gas and dust.

36

Most of the matter lies on a single plane around the sun, giving the solar system the appearance of a huge cartwheel.

To visualize the distribution of matter in the solar system, imagine that the sun were to lose its entire family. Catastrophic? Not to the sun, for it contains 99 9/10 per cent of the material in the solar system.

Considering the size of the sun, the distances at which the planets are spaced seem remarkable. To illustrate this, suppose we placed a twelve-inch sphere representing the sun at one end of a football field. On this scale, we could fit only the first four planets into the field. The others would range out so far that we would have to place Pluto, the farthermost, nearly a mile away.

TABLE 1

Planets	Mean Distance from Sun (millions of miles)	Mean Diameter (miles)	Mass (earth = 1)	Density (water = 1)	Period	
Mercury	36	3,100	0.0543	5.3	88	days
Venus	67	7,750	0.8136	5	225	days
Earth	93	7,970	1.000	5.5	365	days
Mars	142	4,140	0.1069	4	687	days
Jupiter	484	88,000	318.35	1.4	11.9	years
Saturn	887	71,000	95.3	.7	29.4	years
Uranus	1,785	32,000	14.58	1.6	84	years
Neptune	2,800	31,000	17.26	2.3	165	years
Pluto	3,675	3,700	1.000?	5?	248	years

The planets' spacing from the sun is most easily expressed in terms of the *astronomical unit,* which is the earth's mean distance from the sun—about 93,000,000 miles. Taking the earth's distance as one astronomical unit, planetary distances from the sun are as shown in the third column of Table 2. Since the earth's distance corresponds roughly to 100,000,000 miles, approximate distances of the planets can be found easily by multiplying the astronomical unit values by 100.

Instead of being spaced out evenly, distance from one planet to another becomes successively greater, in some cases doubling with each step. This leads to a curious numerical relationship known as Bode's Law, although it is not a physical law. J. D. Titius discovered the relationship, but J. E. Bode, editor of the *Astronomical Journal,* brought it into prominence in 1772. First, take the numbers 0, 3, 6, 12, 24, 48, 96, 192, and 384, each of which (except the first two) is double the preceding number. Now add 4 to each and divide by 10. Taking the earth's distance as 1, the list of numbers we have made comes remarkably close to predicting the planetary distances in astronomical units. The relationship, which predicted the discovery of Uranus and the asteroid belt, breaks down for Neptune and Pluto. It is not known whether this relationship is fundamental or merely an accident. However, it is a simple way to remember planetary distances.

TABLE 2

Planets	Bode's Law	True Distance
Mercury	0.4	0.4
Venus	0.7	0.7
Earth	1.0	1.0
Mars	1.6	1.5
Asteroid (Ceres)	2.8	2.77
Jupiter	5.2	5.2
Saturn	10.0	9.5
Uranus	19.6	19.2
Neptune	38.8	30.1
Pluto	77.2	39.5

Measured by Pluto's orbit, the planetary cartwheel is eight billion miles across. But this is only a fraction of its actual size as measured by its farthest-ranging members, the comets. They travel more than 1,000 times Pluto's distance from the sun.

In size, comets are the sun's largest satellites, some with diameters exceeding even that of Jupiter, the largest planet. However, the material of comets is very tenuous, being mostly gas surrounding a nucleus which averages only a mile or so in diameter. It would take billions of them to equal the mass of the earth.

Comets have been called "flying gravel banks" and "icebergs of space" because they apparently accumulate from debris consisting of frozen water and gases, such as methane and ammonia, and from cosmic dust and gravel. Thin clouds of this debris lie far beyond the planets at the outermost limits of the solar system. As comets condense from this material, they start accelerating slowly toward the sun, picking up speed over the years until they are hurtling toward the inner solar system at 100,000 to 200,000 miles an hour. When a comet nears and swings around the sun, its gases vaporize and expand, giving the appearance of great size. Some of the vaporized material is so thin that the pressure of sunlight pushes it away from the comet, creating a tail that might be 100,000,000 miles long and 10,000,000 miles wide. After rounding the sun, the comet again shoots far into space.

There is evidence that comets may be responsible for some of the meteor showers we run into occasionally. A few of these cosmic hailstorms have been identified with the orbits of comets, two of them with the famous Halley's comet which is due to make a return visit to the inner solar system in 1986. The theory is this: On each visit to the sun the comet disintegrates a little more, losing some of its solid particles from the central mass. The particles eventually become strewn along the comet's entire orbit and spread out by the gravitational effect of the planets. The earth experiences a meteor shower when it crosses paths with this debris.

The term "meteor" refers to the bright streak a particle leaves as it burns up in the atmosphere. Those objects which reach the earth are called *meteorites*. Few of the objects survive the trip through the atmosphere.

This rubble from space probably has many sources, despite evidence linking some of it with comets. The meteorites are stone and iron bodies with densities which indicate they must have formed under high pressures and temperatures that could occur only inside small planets.

There is reason to believe that the asteroid belt may be a source of meteorites. The belt is composed of thousands of small, irregularly shaped bodies traveling in orbits located between Mars and Jupiter. The larger asteroids, ranging up to nearly 500 miles in diameter, have been tracked with telescopes. Before the asteroids were discovered, computations showed another planet should exist between Mars and Jupiter. The asteroids may be the remains of a planet broken up by Jupiter's gravitational pull, or the pieces of two planets which collided. The belt is a sort of natural boundary between the inner and outer planets.

Genesis

When we picture the solar system in its true proportions, man's concern with devising various ways in which the planets could have formed around the sun seems slightly ridiculous, in a way (with apologies to the hardworking theorists), for the planets appear as mere droplets shed by the behemoth star as it rushes through space.

"Why all the complicated theories?" we might be tempted to ask. "Surely, given such a huge, churning mass, a few drops are bound to be spilled."

In seeking to determine the origin of the earth, all modern theories consider the beginning of the entire solar system, including the sun. There are two reasons for this approach. For one thing, most of the solar system's material is concentrated in the sun. For another, the relationships and regularities involved point to a common origin.

Here are some of the clues scholars consider in devising ways to explain the origin of the solar system:

• The planets all move in the same direction around the sun (counterclockwise, using north-star orientation).

• All of the planets (except Uranus*) spin in the same direction in which they revolve.

• The planetary orbits are nearly circular.

• The orbits lie nearly in the same plane.

• Tilt of the planets' axes to this plane (with the exception of Uranus) is small.

• Most of the moons revolve about the planets in the same direction in which the planets themselves spin and move around the sun.

As a result of these considerations, most recent theories suppose that the solar system was once a massive, slowly rotating cloud of gas and dust. Given such a cloud, the sun should have formed as follows:

The cloud contracted slowly under gravitational force. As this happened, streams of matter spiraled toward the central core, imparting additional rotation which flattened the cloud into a disc. The temperature of the core began to rise under the tremendous compression exerted by the accumulating matter. Eventually, the temperature of the central mass became high enough to ignite the cycle of nuclear reactions which is the source of energy of all stars. When the proto-

---

* Axes of all the planets are tilted, but Uranus is flopped over so far in relation to the other planets that it appears to us to rotate backwards.

sun began generating its own energy, a counterforce arose within it—gas pressure. This outward pressure eventually stopped gravitational contraction, and the sun reached the state of equilibrium in which we see it today.

Stillborn Stars?

As for the planets, the theories differ in detail as to how they formed, but all agree they came about as a result of condensations within a nebula surrounding the sun. One of the most popular current ideas is that within the swirling, contracting cloud of the protosun, there were areas of minor turbulence—eddies—which formed the protoplanets and protomoons.

These lesser condensations were too small in mass to build up the internal pressures and temperatures necessary to start nuclear reactions, so they cooled and solidified. In a sense, the planets are stillborn stars.

One widely held theory in the past was that the planets were born when another star either grazed or passed very close to ours, pulling out a filament of solar material which eventually cooled into globules. What we now know about the properties of stars rules out this idea. The gas in stars exists under terrific heat and pressure. If some were scooped out and thrown into the vacuum of space, it would explode rather than condense.

Actually, we may consider the exact mechanism by which the planets were created as somewhat beside the point in the larger philosophical view. For there is increasing evidence that they are a natural byproduct of stellar formation, and not the result of unusual events. Thus, the sun's collection of planetary debris is thought to be the rule, rather than the exception, among the stars.

Any theory of planetary creation must explain certain peculiar characteristics of the solar system. These include the striking arrangement of the planets as to size and composition. The inner planets are small, with diameters ranging from 3,100 to 7,970 miles (Table 1). The outer planets—with the exception of Pluto, which may be a moon escaped from Neptune—are gigantic in comparison.

But while the inner planets are small, their average densities are high. The earth, which may be densest of all, is five and one-half times as dense as water. Mercury, Venus, and Mars are only a little less dense.

The outer planets, on the other hand, are comparative lightweights. Saturn is so light that it would float if it could be dropped into a huge ocean. It is only seven-tenths as dense as water. Jupiter, bigger than all the other planets put together, is only a little denser than water.

Two other peculiarities give added significance to the picture: distribution of moons among the planets and density of planetary atmospheres.

The planets nearest the sun have relatively few moons, whereas the other planets have an abundance of moons. Mercury and Venus have no moons; the earth has one; Mars, two; Jupiter, twelve; Saturn, nine; Uranus, five; Neptune, two; and Pluto, none.

As for atmospheres, the inner planets have thin gaseous shells, while the outer ones have extremely thick atmospheric layers. The atmospheres of the giant planets may account for most of their size, one theory holding that they consist of small rock and metal cores overlaid by thousands of miles of frozen gases and water.

How are these things explained? There are two ideas: One is that the big planets were formed much larger than the others in the first place and, therefore, had more gravitational attraction with which to attract and hold the lighter elements. The giant planets are believed to consist mainly of hydrogen, the lightest element, hence their low-average density. The other theory is that the inner planets, being

43

much closer to the sun, were subjected to much more heat before the sun contracted to its present size, causing their lighter elements, as well as their moons, to "boil" away.

Evaporation of the lighter elements from the planets also has been used to explain why some moons circle their planets in the direction opposite that in which their parent bodies spin and move around the sun. The theory is this: All of the planets lost some mass as a result of evaporation in the early, hot days of formation. Decrease in mass, and, therefore, gravitational attraction, allowed the moons to move farther from their parent bodies, with the result that some escaped and wandered away. These were captured by other planets to become the "maverick" moons, which revolve clockwise around their planets. They include Saturn's Phoebe, Neptune's Triton, and four of Jupiter's satellites, designated VIII, IX, XI, and XII.

The Sun's "Life Belt"

Fortunately, through all our gyrations in the solar system and galaxy, we remain within a "life belt" surrounding our star. This belt is the temperate zone around the sun in which conditions favorable for life could occur. Two other planets lie within this area—Venus and Mars. In the chapter on planetary exploration we shall investigate the possibilities of finding life in and outside this zone.

IV. SPACESHIPS

ROCKET and automobile engines, at least those in most common use, have a basic similarity: Both are internal-combustion engines using the burning of a fuel-oxygen mixture to produce hot gases which create tremendous pressures.

The similarity ends there, but it is useful to compare the two. In the automobile, the gases push a piston which, through a series of links, eventually pushes a wheel against the ground. In the rocket, the gases push, not on the ground or even the air, but directly on the vehicle itself, that is, the forward end of the combustion chamber, making the rocket, in effect, a single, huge piston. The rocket thus provides its own "internal push," and can travel in a vacuum where there is nothing else to push against.

Another important difference between the two is the matter of how they obtain oxygen with which to burn their fuel. The automobile merely sucks it from the air. But the rocket, designed to operate in space, must carry its own supply in one form or another. The chemical rocket, therefore, carries two *propellants—fuel* * and *oxidizer*.

The fundamentals of rocketry are contained in the three

* Rocket engineers often use the word "fuel" in place of "propellants" to avoid awkward language. We shall do likewise here.

laws of motion expressed by Sir Isaac Newton in the seventeenth century:

- A motionless body remains at rest or a moving body remains in motion along a straight line at constant speed unless acted upon by some other force.
- A force acting upon a body causes it to accelerate in the direction of the force. The acceleration is directly proportional to the force and inversely proportional to the mass (weight) of the body.
- For every action, there is an equal and opposite reaction.

The third law states the basic principle of rocket propulsion, but it sometimes causes confusion among the uninitiated, who see in it the implication that the rocket exhaust acts on something outside the rocket, causing a push in the opposite direction. The law simply describes the recoil phenomenon familiar to anyone who has fired a rifle. The rifle is kicked back because of the force which expels the bullet, not because of the bullet pushing against the air as it leaves the rifle. Recoil, what Newton's law calls reaction, is what propels a rocket. We may liken a rocket to a gun which fires continuously to produce a steady recoil or *thrust*.

A look at what goes on inside a rocket engine will fix these ideas more firmly in mind. The pressures created in the combustion chamber push with equal force on all walls of the chamber. If the chamber was closed, the equal forces in all directions would counteract each other and there would be no movement. But the gases are allowed to escape at one end, the nozzle, leaving thrust only at the opposite end of the chamber.

Despite all the technical description and citing of Newton's law, it still may be difficult to accept the fact that the roaring Niagara of flame shooting from the rocket nozzle contributes no additional thrust by striking the ground or air. The reason goes right back to the third law: The exhaust gases must be allowed to escape as quickly as possible, for the greater the speed, or force, toward the rear, the greater the equal and opposite reaction. Hindrance of any sort defeats this purpose. Hence, a rocket develops 10 to 15 per cent more thrust in space than it does within the atmosphere.

From the foregoing, it is apparent that one way to increase thrust is to increase *exhaust velocity*. Another way is to increase the mass of propellant discharged every second. The same thrust results from shooting out 100 pounds of propellant at 1,000 miles an hour as from ejecting twice as much at half that speed. Obviously, the propulsion engineer prefers the first way since it means thrust can be increased (Momentum = Mass × Velocity) without carrying additional heavy fuel into space.

It seems fitting that the term "horsepower" is passé as far as Space-Age vehicles are concerned. Ask a rocket man how much horsepower a particular rocket engine produces and he's likely to look vaguely uneasy for a moment while searching for a reply, for it means little to him. As he contemplates 220,000 pounds of deadweight *Titan I* missile pushing down on the launch pad, he is concerned with how much sheer push must be exerted straight up to get the vehicle launched. It is logical for him to compute this push, or thrust, in pounds.

In order to boost itself from the ground, a rocket's thrust must exceed its loaded weight by about 30 per cent. Another way of saying this is that it must have a *thrust-to-weight ratio* of 1.3. This applies, of course, only when a rocket is launched from the earth's surface. Once in space, where it has overcome the major pull of the earth's gravity and is traveling at thousands of miles an hour, even a small push can accelerate a rocket. *Titan I*, with a first-stage thrust of some 300,000 pounds, has a ratio of about 1.4 at launch.

The thrust-to-weight ratio changes, of course, as propellants are consumed and ejected, enabling a rocket to climb more efficiently second by second. But engineers are never satisfied. They face the fact that the greatest portion of a rocket's gross weight is its propellant load, which runs up to 90 per cent for multistage vehicles designed to hurl satellites and space probes aloft. Engines of the biggest rockets, such as *Titan* and *Atlas,* burn hundreds of gallons of fuel in each second of operation. Engineers thus seek the most efficient fuels possible, those packing the most "push per pound."

More technically, this measure of rocket performance is known as *specific impulse,* the number of pounds of thrust produced by burning one pound of propellant per second. The most energetic propellants in current use deliver a specific impulse of about 400—that is, if one pound of propellant is burned in one second, the result is 400 pounds of thrust.

If specific impulse is improved, a rocket requires less propellant load and, therefore, less deadweight structure to support it, and speed, range, and payload capability can be increased. Some chemicals theoretically are capable of specific impulses up to 450 or 475. To improve performance beyond that, engineers must turn to other systems of propulsion, for the power produced by chemical combustion is limited by the chemical binding energies of the substances involved.

Another measure of rocket performance is the fueled-weight-to-empty-weight ratio, or *mass ratio,* of a given vehicle. One of the most important goals in rocket research is to improve this ratio in order to have the greatest amount of propellant pushing the least amount of deadweight. If a rocket weighs, say, 90,000 pounds with its full propellant load and 30,000 pounds empty, its mass ratio is 3 to 1. Such a vehicle is capable of achieving a maximum speed at least equal to its exhaust velocity before running out of fuel. Exhaust velocities of current rockets run some 5,000 miles per hour. In order to go twice its exhaust velocity, a rocket must have a mass ratio of 7.4 to 1. A ratio of 20 to 1 enables a rocket to reach three times its exhaust velocity.

Rocket engineers have gone to great lengths to improve mass ratios. Since propellant tanks are a major part of the rocket structure, they have been made as thin-walled as possible, so thin, in fact, that missiles such as *Atlas* and *Titan* would warp or collapse under their own weight if it weren't for the stiffening effect of the internal pressure exerted by propellants.

Rocket performance can be improved further by staging, which essentially is a means of improving efficiency by getting rid of unnecessary mass as soon as it no longer is needed. Stages usually are piled one atop another. The bottom stage, or booster rocket, lifts the entire vehicle up until its tanks are empty and then drops off. With the remaining stage or stages moving at the booster's maximum velocity, the next stage fires, and so on until the final stage, or payload, is moving with the sum of the velocities reached by each stage. Four- and five-stage rockets have been used to launch satellites and space probes.

Since chemical rockets are the most commonly used, it is worth knowing that there are two classes of chemical rockets—liquid and solid.

Liquid rockets ordinarily use two separate propellants, both in liquid form. The fuel may be kerosene, gasoline, alcohol, hydrazine, liquid hydrogen, or a number of other high-energy substances. The oxidizer may be pure oxygen, usually in the liquid form known in the jargon of rocketry as LOX.

The liquid rocket has been called a plumber's nightmare. Since most liquid propellants are highly explosive, they must be stored in separate tanks and not allowed to come in contact before injection into the combustion chamber. They also require an elaborate system of pipes, pumps, and valves which add not only undesirable vehicle weight but great complexity in handling and operation. If a liquid rocket uses the most desirable propellants, it cannot be loaded at leisure and set aside for future use. The most energetic propellants often are the most corrosive and, therefore, cannot be left long in the system. LOX is noncorrosive, but since it must be kept at −297 degrees F. to keep it from boiling away, it can freeze valves. All of this means that a liquid rocket must be fueled on the launch pad, a dangerous, tricky business requiring painstaking precautions.

In contrast, the solid-propellant rocket has the simplicity of a bullet. Fuel and oxidizer—contained in such combinations as nitroglycerin-nitrocellulose or polyurethane-aluminum-ammonium perchlorate—are mixed together in a single, solid, rubbery mass—the *grain*—and packed into a rocket case. When a nozzle is attached to one end, the rocket is essentially complete and ready for firing. Propellants are less explosive and corrosive in the solid state, so a solid rocket can be stored in a ready-to-fire condition for long periods of time.

Despite their obvious shortcomings in this comparison, liquid rockets are superior in several major respects. For one thing, liquid propellants inherently pack more push per pound. One of the fundamental laws concerning the nature of materials is that the most energetic substances are gases, the next most active are liquids, and the least energetic are solids. The thrust per pound of a solid propellant is about 75 to 80 per cent of that obtained from a pound of liquid propellant.

The burning of liquid propellants also is easier to control and cut off, a vital matter in many space missions where thrust must be terminated sharply at the exact moment a desired velocity is reached. This can be done by simply regulating a valve in a liquid rocket, but cutting off a solid

50

rocket's combustion is a problem comparable to extinguishing a blaze in a mattress. It is done by such methods as blowing off the nozzle or dropping combustion-chamber pressure sharply by opening vents in the walls.

The liquid rocket, because its thrust can be finely controlled, is more easily applied to manned space travel. It has, in fact, been used experimentally for manned flight for some time, dating back to the first rocket-powered aircraft. For that matter, a jet aircraft engine is a rocket—the only basic difference between it and a missile engine is that it doesn't carry its own oxidizer and, therefore, must operate within the atmosphere.

Solids hold the advantage over liquids where overall ease of handling and launching are paramount. An example of this is the Navy's intermediate-range, two-stage *Polaris* missile. As a weapon designed to be carried and launched by a submarine, its advantages over liquid-propelled rockets are apparent. Other examples include missiles designed to be transported and launched under battlefield or air-warfare conditions, such as the Army's two-stage *Pershing* and the Air Force's *Falcon*. For fast, easy handling and launching in an ICBM, the Air Force has produced the solid-fueled, three-stage *Minuteman*.

Where large rockets are concerned, the solids offer a unique advantage—they can be made in easily transportable segments and then bolted together for firing. A further advantage here is that the number of segments can be varied, allowing a choice of rocket size.

Liquid and solid propellants can be combined to good advantage in multistage satellite-launching rockets. They can also be combined in the same rocket, with a liquid oxidizer fed into a solid fuel, resulting in a *hybrid* rocket. Hybrids don't produce as much push per pound as the liquids, but they are as easily controlled.

There are liquid propellants that are "storable," that is,

they can be put in a rocket and kept there for some time without damaging the system. But as a rule, those that are storable are not the most powerful chemicals.

We have noted that the most thrust we can expect from the process of chemical combustion is about 475 pounds per pound of propellant. To improve rocket performance beyond that we must turn to other sources of energy.

Immediately we think of nuclear energy. A power source that can drive a submarine around the world on a mere handful of fuel seems made to order for the voracious demands of rocket ships. (Plate 4.)

But there are some stubborn facts of space travel to consider. While a nuclear reactor can produce great quantities of heat, that alone is not enough to drive a rocket. Any reaction engine must have *working fluid*—something must be ejected backward in order to produce thrust. Unlike an atomic submarine, which is immersed in a working fluid it can push against, a nuclear rocket still faces the necessity of carrying along its own working fluid—propellant—with which to push itself.

Equipping a rocket with a reactor does eliminate one propellant—the oxidizer—since heat is produced without combustion. Otherwise, a high-thrust nuclear rocket operates on the same propulsion principle as a chemical vehicle—the propellant is heated to a gaseous state and exhausted through a nozzle to obtain thrust. The most desirable propellant for this purpose is hydrogen. As the lightest element it is capable of high exhaust velocities. Heated up to 4,000 degrees F. in a reactor, it can produce a specific impulse two to three times that of chemical rockets.

This certainly is a healthy improvement. But for manned space travel, the nuclear rocket presents an even healthier weight problem—the heavy shielding required to protect crews from radiation.

What the foregoing adds up to is that nuclear energy,

capable of such spectacular results elsewhere, seems somewhat less than that when applied to space. Despite all the energy available to it, the nuclear rocket engine still is a slave to a burden of propellant. And while producing significantly greater thrust, it does so at the expense of as much as twenty times the weight of the chemical rocket.

No wonder that during the early years of the Space Age some of the more conservative thinkers threw a good deal of cold water on the idea of harnessing the atom to spaceships. It was pointed out, and rightly, that much of the advantage of nuclear energy was lost as far as space travel was concerned.

Nevertheless, the problem got the close scrutiny it deserved, and it soon became apparent that the nuclear engine's greater performance more than makes up for its greater weight where the more difficult space missions are concerned, actually enabling it to pack big payloads for *less* gross weight.

A comparison of vehicle requirements for a manned trip to Mars from earth orbit shows that the nuclear rocket offers spectacular improvement after all—a chemical rocket might weigh 10,000,000 pounds, whereas a nuclear ship would weigh only one-tenth as much. The chemical rocket, in having to carry and pump two weighty propellants while producing only one-half or one-third of the engine performance, comes off second best over the long haul.

We might liken the nuclear rocket to a diesel truck—it cannot display its power or economy by delivering small packages over short distances.

There are other suggested approaches to a high-thrust nuclear rocket, using the explosive force of small atomic bombs instead of a reactor. In the simplest case, "capsule" bombs would be exploded against the heavily reinforced and shielded rear end of a rocket. In another, the capsules would be detonated in a huge water-filled chamber perhaps more than 100 feet in diameter. The explosions would eject the water to produce thrust.

So far, we have discussed only high-thrust rockets, those powerful enough to take off from the earth by themselves. They are necessary for getting into space in the first place. However, they are at a certain disadvantage once there, for the first and most difficult part of the climb against gravity burns up most of their propellant in the first few minutes of flight. Thereafter, they are obliged to coast powerless through space, taking days to reach the moon, months to reach the nearest planets and years to travel to the outermost bodies of the solar system. Any propellant carried along, even in multistage vehicles, is strictly for short trajectory-correction blasts and, depending upon the mission, for "braking" to land and then launching again to return home. This applies to high-thrust nuclear as well as chemical rockets; both must haul huge loads of propellant into space.

The fact that it takes so much fuel to get into space has led to proposals for "orbital refueling" in which a spaceship bound on an interplanetary mission would blast into orbit at 18,000 miles an hour several hundred miles above the earth and refuel from an orbiting tanker before continuing on its journey. But while this would enable a ship to increase its final speed and mission capability, it still would not provide enough propellant to permit continuous thrust for interplanetary flight.

Couldn't the propulsion systems we have discussed be throttled back to a more economical cruising thrust, once in space? They could, perhaps, but they still would require enormous amounts of propellant. The situation calls for a different kind of rocket, one powered by a *low-thrust* propulsion system.

The low-thrust rocket achieves great fuel economy by shooting out extremely small amounts of propellant at speeds

54

up to forty times the exhaust velocity possible with conventional rockets. The result is very low thrust, perhaps no more than a couple of pounds. And since a lot of power is needed to produce the high exhaust velocities, another result is *tons* of engine to produce mere *pounds* of thrust.

This situation seems ridiculous at first glance, but as one expert, John G. Lee, research director of United Aircraft Corporation research laboratories, has pointed out:

> ... if you could push on a 5,000-pound object with no friction, using a force of only one pound, the object would achieve a speed of about one-quarter of a mile per hour in the first minute. At the end of the first hour it would reach a speed of 15 miles per hour, and at the end of the first day it would be over 375 miles per hour. In a month it would have attained the speed of 11,000 miles per hour, and in about two months it would have attained escape velocity. When you boost [a] ... vehicle out of the atmosphere at perhaps 15,000 miles per hour and continue to add an additional 11,000 miles per hour every month, it soon becomes apparent that you have reached velocities at least as high as those likely to be reached by any other devices.[*]

Such a rocket cannot, of course, take off from the earth's surface; it must be lofted into space by a high-thrust engine. But once put into space its continuous push enables vast improvement in both speed and payload-carrying capability over the rocket which merely coasts through space.

What a picayunish amount of steady thrust can do appears quite spectacular when we compare travel times of high- and low-thrust rockets for some of the longer missions within the solar system. The 3.6-billion-mile trip to Pluto, for example, might take forty to fifty years in a conventional

[*] *The Missile Industry—In Defense and the Exploration of Space* (Baltimore: The Martin Company, 1961). A compilation of a series of lectures before the New York Society of Security Analysts by The Martin Company and United Aircraft Corporation.

high-thrust vehicle, but less than three in a low-thrust rocket which had a continuous thrust of only one pound after escaping from the earth.

There are various types of proposed low-thrust systems, including ion, plasmajet, photon rockets, and the so-called solar-propulsion vehicles. The first three often are called electric rockets because they involve production of electricity. Since large amounts of electricity are required, nuclear or thermonuclear reactors, which would provide heat to drive electric generators, appear to be the most likely energy sources for such rockets.

The ion rocket is a good example of the fuel economy possible with low-thrust systems. An ion engine with less than one-half pound of thrust would require only 1,000 pounds of propellant for a 300-day trip to Mars from an orbit around the earth. A conventional chemically propelled rocket would require up to ten times as much fuel for the trip.

The ion engine is so named because it uses charged atoms, known as ions, as propellant. Ions are simply electric charges which are attracted or repelled by electric fields, making it possible to shoot them from a rocket nozzle at extremely high speeds. An alkali metal heated to a vapor, such as cesium, provides the fuel, or *ion source,* for such a propulsion system.

In the plasma rocket, thrust is obtained by discharging an electric arc through a propellant, such as hydrogen. The resulting hot gas has been *ionized* and is called a *plasma.* Gas in this state conducts electricity and can be contained and directed by magnetic fields. This leads to the possibility that the gas in a rocket engine can be kept from touching the walls of the chamber by magnetic fields, meaning that engine performance no longer need be limited by the melting temperature of its walls; higher propellant temperatures and correspondingly higher performance can be attained.

While ion and plasma rockets are entirely feasible and

development on them is well under way, the photon rocket is a much more ambitious undertaking. The propellant for such a rocket would be particles of light (photons), which, of course, would provide the highest possible exhaust velocity, 186,000 miles per second. There is nothing really fantastic about such an idea except the intensity of the beam that would have to be generated and the power source that would be required. A comet's tail, as already noted, is formed by the pressure of sunlight, and even a flashlight beam exerts an infinitesimal thrust. The big practical difficulty in development of such a propulsion system is the size of the power plant needed to produce a sufficiently intense light beam. This seems prohibitive unless total conversion of matter to energy could be achieved.

A far simpler way of using light to produce thrust, one which already has been tested with a U.S. satellite, is a solar propulsion method known as *solar sailing*. A space vehicle propelled in this fashion is pushed by sunlight exactly as a sailboat is pushed by the wind. The orbit of the *Echo I* satellite, a large, lightweight balloon, was slightly affected by the pressure of sunlight, which in the vicinity of the earth exerts a push of about five pounds per square mile of surface.

That incident, however, was not a practical demonstration of solar sailing, and it appears that the payload such a vehicle could carry would be quite small in relation to the dimensions of the sail surface required.

Another method of directly harnessing the sun's energy for propulsion would be to heat hydrogen gas by solar radiation and exhaust it through a conventional rocket nozzle. While this method would eliminate the equipment associated with heating by chemical or nuclear means, it would need a large optical system for collecting and converting radiation energy to heat, with the result that thrust per weight would be very low.

Obviously, space travel requires at least two kinds of propulsion schemes—high-thrust systems for leaping into space from the earth, and the low, continuous-thrust systems to take over afterwards. Spaceships intended for long interplanetary round trips must use both kinds.

Although some of the propulsion systems we have discussed seem extremely advanced, the Space Age is just beginning, and if space technology develops at only half the pace set by aeronautical technology, the advances of the next ten, twenty, and fifty years unquestionably will result in achievements as spectacular to us today as supersonic jet transport would have been to the world of 1912. That was the year *Scientific American* magazine reported: "To affirm that the airplane is going to revolutionize the future is to be guilty of the wildest exaggeration."

The odds are that the technology of space travel will advance several times faster than did the know-how of air travel. As a matter of fact, that has been the case to date, and we really shouldn't expect it to be otherwise, for the rule of technological progress for good or bad is that each new technology begets an ever-greater speed of development.

V. SPACESHIPS AND THE LAW

THE most important "law" affecting space travel is this: The ordinary laws of physics that we have discovered here on earth apply everywhere else in the universe.

This may seem an obvious, even trivial, thing to point out, but it is a very powerful statement of science, for it says that the mathematical equations we have found to describe the fundamental properties of motion, energy, and matter in our tiny bit of space are universal, applying to the moon, to other planets, and to other stars and galaxies. It also says that these rules apply to a rocket, whether shot a few miles over the earth's surface or a billion miles into space.

Man wasn't ready for space travel until he realized this, for not many centuries ago he looked out on the rest of the universe and thought that the earth probably was unique; for all he knew, everything "out there" might be subject to completely alien forces. It took the genius of Newton to deduce that the mysterious force which caused the fall of a rock was the same force that governed the motion of the moon, the earth, and every other object in the universe, and that it could be described by a simple equation. And it wasn't until this century that Einstein concluded that the velocity of light must be the same no matter where measured and is the top limiting speed of the universe.

Gravity and Escape from Earth

Newton's law, as noted earlier, states that all bodies in the universe, from the smallest particle to the largest star, attract each other, and that the force of attraction depends upon the masses of the bodies and their distance apart. This says that a spaceship must work hardest during the first part of its climb from the earth, and is subject to gravitational pull no matter where it travels.

As far as leaving the earth is concerned, an object does not escape from our planet's gravitational pull until it leaves the earth-moon system. Thus, an artificial satellite does not escape from the earth (although it escapes from the surface for perhaps an indefinite period of time), nor does a rocket which lands on the moon. In both cases, the earth's gravitational field remains predominant. A rocket escapes from the earth when, in effect, it becomes a tiny man-made planet, subject primarily to the gravitational influence of the sun.

In theory a space vehicle with some means of continuous propulsion could escape from the earth with no more speed than a small boy can work up on a bicycle. But this would be extremely wasteful of energy, so it is necessary to blast an object to tremendous speed, quickly building up the momentum necessary to carry it from the earth.

The minimum speed required to do this from a standing start on the earth's surface is seven miles per second, or 25,000 miles an hour, and it is called *escape velocity*. This is defined as the speed an object must reach in order to coast away from the earth *without further propulsion* following its initial short blast from the earth's surface. The speed is the same for a rocket or a rock.

The problem of escaping into space is similar to that which confronts a cyclist who sees a steep hill ahead and builds up as much speed as possible in the hope that momentum will help him reach the top.

To satisfy ourselves that a slow-speed escape, starting from the earth's surface, would be most impractical, let us examine how the constant pull of gravity affects a rocket during its climb. Any rocket, regardless of its size or power, suffers a loss in acceleration due to the backward pull of gravity during the time required to reach escape velocity. This is called *gravitational loss*. Specifically, any rocket is retarded by twenty miles an hour for *each second* it spends accelerating to escape velocity. If, for example, it spends 200 seconds reaching escape speed, it suffers an efficiency loss totaling 4,000 miles an hour.

This effect may be likened to walking up an escalator that is moving *down*. If you walk up quickly, you will have fewer steps to climb than if you walk up slowly. The less time you spend on the escalator, the less efficiency you lose to its downward motion. Similarly, the less time a rocket spends accelerating to escape velocity, the less gravitational loss affects it.

Achievement of escape velocity does not mean that a rocket actually has escaped at that moment from the earth's gravitational pull or that it can maintain that speed after fuel burnout. Escape velocity is a sort of magic number in the sense that once a rocket has reached that speed it will not fall back to earth after power cutoff. Although slowed considerably by the earth's pull following fuel burnout, it has enough momentum left to carry it to the top of "gravity hill" where the gravitational influence of the sun becomes predominant.

Every celestial body has an escape velocity which depends upon the strength of its gravitational field (its mass). To escape from the moon, an object would need a velocity of

61

only one and a half miles per second. The escape velocity on Venus is about six miles a second, and that on Mars is three miles per second. The largest planet, Jupiter, has an escape velocity of thirty-seven miles per second.

Free Fall and Weightlessness

In Chapter I we mentioned that there is no such thing as "gravity-free" space, although the term often is used in explaining the phenomenon of weightlessness. The term "zero gravity," also used in this connection, is equally misleading. Actually, you need not escape from the earth in order to experience weightlessness in exactly the same way that it occurs in space flight. You have only to jump from a chair or a diving board, or fall out of bed. For that matter, when you leap upward you are weightless from the instant your feet leave the ground.

The condition of weightlessness is the result of what is technically known as "unrestricted motion in a gravitational field." So by definition it is a phenomenon that occurs in the presence of gravity.

The kind of motion is what counts. As we stand on the earth, gravity is constantly trying to pull us down. But our downward movement is restricted by the earth's solid surface, so we feel this restricted motion as "weight."

Unrestricted motion also is known as *free fall*. Here, again, is a term which may be confusing since most of us are used to thinking of "fall" as meaning only downward motion. But as far as the space scientist is concerned, you can fall in any direction, up as well as down.

A better choice of words might be "free motion." This means motion that is unhampered—and unaided—affected only by gravitational pull. Thus, men traveling in space become weightless only when their vehicle is coasting without propulsion, subject solely to the force of gravity. The direction in which the vehicle is moving, whether toward or away from the gravitating body, or in orbit about it, doesn't matter, nor does its speed or the strength of the gravitational pull. As soon as propulsion is applied, however, "weight" is felt—not in the direction of the gravitating body, but in the direction from which the push is applied. How much weight is felt depends upon the strength of the thrust.

A feeling of some weight can be achieved for space travelers by imparting a spin to their vehicle. In this way, centrifugal force creates an artificial gravity.

An airplane pilot doesn't become weightless when he cuts off his power and glides because the atmosphere is supporting the aircraft—restricting its downward motion. But weightlessness can be achieved for a few moments in an airplane by pulling the craft up into a sharp climb and then cutting back the power so that it floats around the top of a parabolic curve.

Motion in Space

A spaceship that is coasting through space without propulsion is in free fall and, therefore, subject to the same laws that govern planetary motion. The laws, formulated by Johannes Kepler in the seventeenth century, are:

• The planets revolve about the sun in elliptical orbits, with the sun at one focus.

• The line joining the center of the sun to the center of a planet "sweeps out" equal areas in equal periods of time.

• The square of a planet's period ("year") is proportional to the cube of its mean distance from the sun.

These laws, along with Newton's, enable us to calculate the trajectories of rockets to any destination in space.

A rocket which fails to reach escape velocity, by however small amount, will fall back to earth. However, it is possible for a vehicle to counterbalance the earth's pull at speeds lower than escape velocity, and that is by becoming an artificial satellite.

Orbital velocity is the speed necessary to maintain a satellite in orbit at a given distance from its *primary*. The closer the orbit to the primary body, the faster a satellite must move in order to counterbalance gravitational pull.

In the case of the earth, the nearest a satellite can be maintained in orbit for any length of time is about 300 miles, which calls for a speed of 18,000 miles per hour. A satellite placed in an orbit closer to the earth is quickly slowed by atmospheric friction and its orbit is destroyed.

The farther a satellite is placed from the earth, the less speed required to keep it in orbit. At a distance of 22,000 miles, a satellite needs a velocity of only 6,800 miles an hour. The earth's natural satellite, some 250,000 miles distant, is sustained in orbit with a speed of only 2,268 miles per hour, a fraction of the speed already reached by manned vehicles.

It happens that at a distance of 22,000 miles, a satellite launched eastward from the earth makes exactly one circuit every twenty-four hours. Since this coincides with the earth's rotation, the effect is that the satellite forever travels over the same spot on the earth's surface, thereby appearing to remain stationary.

If you were riding in a satellite and wanted to move slower in orbit, you would first have to speed up. Conversely, if you wanted to move faster, you would have to slow down. This may seem odd at first glance, but it is quite logical: If a satellite is speeded up, the added centrifugal force will cause it to move farther from the earth and take up a new, larger orbit where it doesn't have to move so fast to counterbalance gravity. So the final result of speeding up your satellite will be to make it travel slower. On the other hand, if you fired a retro-rocket to slow your satellite's orbital speed, it would be drawn inward, and, due to the greater gravitational pull,

64

have to move faster than it did before in order to remain in orbit.

There are four kinds of orbits: circular, elliptical, parabolic, and hyperbolic, all corresponding to the conic sections, or basic curves derived by intersecting a cone with a plane.

The first two types form closed loops about a primary body. The other two form partial, or open, curves, meaning that an object in such an orbit will make only a partial circuit around a body and then shoot off into space, never to return. Comets often move in such orbits, with the result that we see them only once. Other comets move in huge closed orbits, and return to our portion of the solar system after long intervals.

The word "orbits" usually is associated only with satellites. However, a vehicle traveling anywhere in space is in some kind of orbit. A permanent satellite follows either a circular or elliptical orbit, while a rocket launched with enough speed to escape the earth-moon system assumes either a parabolic or hyperbolic orbit with respect to the earth. Usually, the latter two curves are called "trajectories."

The circular orbit, in which a satellite at all times maintains the same distance from its primary, is impossible to achieve unless the primary body is a perfect sphere. The earth is not a perfect sphere, being about thirteen miles flatter at the poles than at its equatorial waistline. The effect of this added mass around the earth's middle is a slightly greater pull when a satellite passes over it, turning a circular orbit into an ellipse.

In an elliptical orbit, a satellite's speed and distance from the earth are subject to constant change. At its closest approach to earth, a satellite is at *perigee;* at its farthest, it is at *apogee.**

* *Perihelion* and *aphelion,* in the case of the sun's satellites.

A satellite in an elliptical orbit alternately falls toward and climbs away from its primary. As it falls, it gains speed, reaching maximum velocity at perigee. Following closest approach, it shoots away from the primary, gradually slowing under the pull of gravity until it reaches minimum speed at apogee and starts the cycle again. The earth, with a period of one year, reaches perihelion, about 90,000,000 miles, in January, and aphelion, 96,000,000 miles, six months later. It speeds up and slows down by 1,000 miles an hour during one circuit of the sun.

Whether a space vehicle enters a parabolic or hyperbolic trajectory is a matter of speed. If it reaches minimum escape velocity, it will enter a parabolic orbit with respect to the earth and become a satellite of the sun. A spaceship placed in such a trajectory takes up an orbit around the sun at about the same distance as the earth, and, therefore, does not change its distance from the sun enough to reach other planets. Only the hyperbolic trajectory, requiring a speed somewhat greater than minimum escape velocity, enables interplanetary travel.*

The Speed Limit and Consequences

In discussing speed, several questions invariably arise: How fast will spaceships be able to travel? Will they some day reach the speed of light? Will man forever be a prisoner of time, unable in a single lifetime to visit other solar systems which even light takes years to reach?

As far as the near future is concerned, man probably will be doing well to reach speeds of twice the velocity of near-earth satellites, about 36,000 miles an hour. Looking a little further ahead, speeds of eight to ten times that appear within reason. This, while not bad for getting around the solar

* See Chapter VI.

system, still will not permit trips to other planetary systems within a man's lifetime—it would take 10,000 years to reach even the nearest star, Alpha Centauri, which is about four and a half light years away.

According to Einstein's theory, the answer to the second question is that spaceships never will be able to reach light speed of 670,000,000 miles per hour. As noted in Chapter II, Einstein's prediction that mass increases with speed has been borne out in the laboratory. The effect of this is of little consequence at, say, 18,000,000 miles an hour. But at 86 per cent of light speed, about 580,000,000 miles an hour, a spaceship's mass, or resistance to being pushed, would be doubled. And as the ship accelerated beyond that, its mass would multiply so rapidly that it theoretically would become infinite at light speed. Reaching light speed, therefore, would require infinite energy, or more than is available in the entire universe.

Well before reaching light speed, the energy requirement of an accelerating spaceship would outstrip the capability of any power plant we can envision. Complete conversion of matter to energy would be required, in contrast to the small fraction converted by atomic power plants today. Whether such energy liberation will be achieved is purely a matter for speculation at this time, although it is not difficult to find optimism among the experts.

Space enthusiasts have proposed several ways in which manned vehicles could conquer the incredible distances separating us from other stars. One suggestion is to put crews into hibernation or suspended animation for long periods during trips that would require decades or centuries. Another is to build huge "Noah's arks" which would carry entire populations and drift toward other stars for centuries, delivering to destination a generation far removed from that which started the trip. Such proposals are fantastic—and probably will remain just that. Scientific and technical considerations aside, while there are people who will volunteer for almost anything, it is difficult to imagine such journeys being undertaken unless they are forced by some impending disaster in the solar system. For purely scientific research, robot devices would be far superior for such expeditions.

Still another proposal for beating the clock on interstellar voyages—the favorite of some space enthusiasts—would take advantage of the relativistic time slowdown, or time dilatation, discussed earlier. Speed alone would do the trick here, theoretically stretching an ordinary lifetime to hundreds, thousands, millions, or even billions of years, depending upon the velocities and travel times involved. Speeds approaching that of light would be necessary to produce a really appreciable effect. At 86 per cent of light speed, for instance, an astronaut would age at only half the rate he would on earth. As in the case of mass increase and shortening of length, this effect would be multiplied manyfold at still higher speeds, so that an astronaut who made a round trip to a star ten light years distant would have the impression the journey lasted only a few years, or even mere days or hours, depending upon how closely he approached light speed. Earth would record the round trip as having taken twenty years if it were made at light speed.

All of the foregoing ideas regarding interstellar travel still belong in the realm of science fiction. It may well be—and we certainly are tempted to conclude—that man never will travel fast enough for relativistic effects to become appreciable, and, therefore, must remain chained forever to his own planetary system. However, we are cautioned by some of the best scientific minds not to rule out such dreams completely.

The coming of the Space Age has pointed up a rather paradoxical situation with regard to light speed: Where space travel is concerned, it is an awesome, almost unimaginable figure. But when we consider communications, light speed is merely ordinary—and already too slow.

Communications technology long ago reached the ultimate speed with use of electricity and radio waves, both of which travel at light speed. This poses no problem on earth; indeed, we think of telephone and radio communication as "instantaneous." However, almost as soon as we leave the earth this limitation upon the speed of communication becomes painfully obvious, even if we travel only as far as the moon. To be sure, we can flash a radar signal to the moon in about 1.3 seconds and receive the bounced-back echo 1.3 seconds later, for a total two-way delay of only 2.6 seconds. This doesn't seem like much, but it can raise problems where control of unmanned exploration vehicles is concerned. For one thing, there are lunar orbiting and landing maneuvers which require split-second timing. And when a remotely controlled explorer vehicle is crawling about on the moon, its earthbound operator must allow for the lag between the instant the vehicle "sees" things to investigate or avoid and the time the operator receives the information and transmits appropriate control orders. This time lag, added to an operator's own human reaction and decision time, could lead to disastrous results.

The lag becomes a matter of minutes, even hours, where other planets are concerned.

VI. THE HIGHWAYS OF SPACE

WE don't have to grasp Einstein's concept of curved space to realize that the natural, and easiest, way to travel through interplanetary space is along a curve.

The paths rockets must follow in going from one planet to another are affected—we might say "shaped"—by the gravitational pull of the sun and by the fact that the planets are in high-speed rotational and orbital motion. Anything which tries to move from one body to another in a straight line must fight this existing force and motion and pay a heavy price in energy to do so. This is true even if we want to move straight toward the sun.

In view of this, the structure and mechanics of the solar system may seem unfortunate as far as space travel is concerned. However, a closer inspection of the situation reveals important features that are conducive to space travel.

For one thing, a rocket possesses formidable velocities before it is launched. In the case of the earth, a space vehicle shares the planet's rotational speed of 1,000 miles an hour and orbital velocity of 66,600 miles per hour prior to launch. By merely detaching itself from the earth's gravitational hold, a rocket receives these velocities as free boosts along its way.

Location of the planets in nearly the same orbital plane is another natural aid to space flight. Obviously, a rocket benefits most from its planet's orbital speed by launching in the plane of its planet's motion around the sun. The fact that the other planets are in nearly this same plane means a rocket expends much less of its own energy in traveling from one planet to another.

At present and for some time to come we must work with rockets that consume an enormous amount of fuel in reaching the speed necessary to escape from the earth.* And in departing from the earth's gravitational influence, a space vehicle does not, contrary to a popular misconception, retain its 25,000-mile-an-hour escape speed. Actually, it *loses* most of that speed as it coasts upward against the pull of gravity following its short powered flight phase; it manages merely to detach itself from the planet, an act which leaves it with a final speed that is comparable to the earth's orbital velocity. To reach another planet, a spacecraft needs escape velocity plus a little more.

Because of the present limitations of rockets, one of the space scientist's primary concerns is choosing the more economical, or "low energy" trajectories between planets. Most economical are the "minimum energy" trajectories, those in which a rocket coasts during most of its trip through space, applying a minimum of energy at departure from the earth and arrival at the target planet. Using such routes, a rocket takes advantage of any free push it can get in leaving the earth, and then enters an orbit about the sun, becoming a tiny, free-coasting artificial planet for most of its journey.

In defining the minimum-energy route, we might say that in general the closer a spaceship follows the solar system's existing patterns of motion, the more it benefits as far as

* See Chapter IV.

travel economy is concerned. It requires less fuel to take up its flight path and, as a result, can carry more payload per pound of fuel.

It shouldn't be surprising, then, to find that the "easiest" route to another planet is not the shortest, but the longest, the one which curves very gently from the orbit of one planet to the orbit of another, rather than cutting across directly. The route requiring the least effort is one which carries a rocket halfway around the sun, meeting the target planet at a point that is directly across the sun from the vehicle's starting point, as shown in Figure 2. The more a rocket of given size departs from the long, curving trajectory, also called a *transfer ellipse,* or *transfer orbit,* the more fuel it requires—at a sacrifice in payload. In actual practice it is not necessary for our planetary probes to utilize the lowest-energy routes, so they can travel somewhat shorter distances.

A typical minimum-energy flight to Mars covers a distance of 360,000,000 miles, more than ten times the straight-line distance when the earth and Mars are nearest each other. The time for such a coasting trip is about 260 days. In order to travel the shortest route to Mars, a spaceship would have to launch "straight up," so to speak, fighting the combined, in-line gravitational pull of both the earth and the sun. This is the most difficult route, requiring so much energy that it is not feasible with conventional rockets. The flight could be made with continuous propulsion, using the low-thrust rockets described earlier. A direct trajectory to one of the inner planets, traveling *toward* the sun, is at least as difficult for another reason.

Somewhat the same situation—the gently curving path being the easiest—applies even in the case of the relatively short trip to the moon. We could just aim for the moon and fire, leading it slightly as if skeet shooting. But a flight path straight out from the earth's surface is extremely ineffi-

72

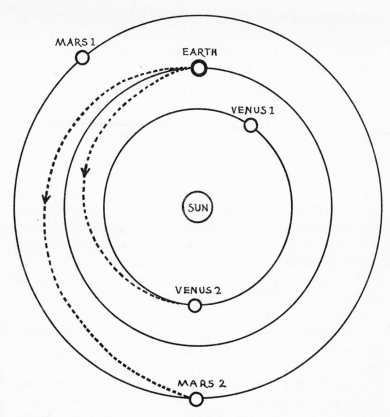

Figure 2. Launch is made with the target planet in position 1, and interception occurs at position 2. Launches are made when these particular planets are near the earth, but not, contrary to a common misconception, to enable rockets to travel the shortest possible routes.

cient.* A rocket adds little of the earth's rotational push to its own forward motion and has a tougher fight against gravity. A better trajectory is one which curves very gently away, almost following the curvature of the earth. A very

* A large, slowly accelerating rocket rises vertically only for the first few minutes of flight, curving over to a shallower and easier rate of climb when speed is sufficient to maintain flight.

efficient trajectory is one which curves nearly halfway around the earth, meaning that the vehicle starts its journey from the side of the earth that is facing away from the moon. In order to take advantage of the earth's spin, a rocket must, of course, launch eastward, the direction in which the earth turns.

In the present state of propulsion technology, travel between planets is possible only by using the planets' orbital speeds to launch a spacecraft on its way. For that matter, even with development of rocketry far beyond its present capability, the earth's orbital speed will remain the primary propulsive force for interplanetary travel. Trips to other planets must be accomplished by *adding to* or *subtracting from* this speed: A rocket going to an outer planet must *add* speed by launching "forward," or in the same direction that earth moves around the sun, while one bound for an inner planet must *subtract* speed by launching "backward," or counter to the earth's orbital motion.

The mechanics of this situation are the same as described earlier for satellite motion: A speed greater than earth's will move a vehicle farther from the sun, toward the outer planets; a speed less than that will result in it being drawn closer

TABLE 3

Mission	Launch Speed	Transit Time
Mercury	29,900 miles per hour	110 days
Venus	25,900	150 days
Mars	25,900	260 days
Jupiter	31,300	2.7 years
Saturn	33,500	6 years
Uranus	34,600	16 years
Neptune	35,300	31 years
Pluto	36,000	46 years
Escape system	36,700	46 years +

74

to the sun, toward the inner planets. In either case, the vehicle travels toward destination in the same direction that the planets move around the sun.

Minimum-energy launch velocities and resulting transit times for various missions are shown in Table 3.

Note that it is just as difficult to travel toward the sun as away from it, that a trip to the innermost planet is almost as hard as traveling out to Jupiter. The reason is that killing off speed in order to travel toward the sun is just as difficult as attaining it. It is worth noting further that a mission to the sun itself is even more difficult than escaping from the solar system, requiring about five times the energy. This should correct another misconception about space travel—that a rocket which misses its target planet will fall into the sun. Such a disaster would occur only if the vehicle somehow lost almost all of its orbital speed around the sun. The fall would require about sixty-four days, starting from the earth's distance from the sun.

One rather surprising fact of space travel is that a minimum-energy flight to another planet requires only a relatively little more launch velocity than a trip to the moon. A rocket bound for the moon must launch with at least 99 per cent of escape velocity, while one going to Mars must add only something like 900 miles an hour to escape speed. This points up the fact that in a lunar flight a spacecraft cannot take advantage of the earth's orbital speed, for the earth and its satellite travel together in space. Only in escaping the earth-moon system does a rocket receive the earth's 66,600-mile-per-hour boost.

Travel to other planets along the lower-energy routes is desirable, of course, only so long as propulsive power remains limited. As advances are made, spaceships will take shorter elliptical paths to the other bodies.

We should emphasize at this point that travel via the minimum-energy trajectories does not necessarily yield the

75

most economical trips where manned space flight is concerned. Travel times are long, and obviously the longer the trip the more deadweight food and other necessities must be carried along. Analysis shows that even without greater propulsive power available, a somewhat shorter (although still low-energy) route can result in a more economical mission. While the more difficult trajectory cuts down a given spacecraft's *total* payload at launch, the shorter flight time reduces the weight of food and supplies in such proportion that a bigger "usable" payload of equipment is delivered to destination.

In addition to the long travel times involved in using the low-energy routes, manned interplanetary flight is further complicated by the waiting period required on another planet before an expedition can start home. With only limited power available, a spaceship dares not launch homeward until the planets are in the proper orbital position. The waiting period required on Mars is 454 days, until Mars, slower of the two planets, is leading the earth in orbit. Return travel time is the same as for the trip out—260 days. So an expedition making this round trip must be prepared to survive away from the earth for more than two years, eight months. With more powerful rockets, waiting periods will be reduced.

With the limitations of chemical rockets, manned interplanetary flight is best accomplished by putting a spaceship in orbit about the earth and refueling it from or attaching it to an added stage that has already been placed in orbit. This enables it to set out with two important advantages—an initial speed of 18,000 miles an hour, and a full load of fuel. It can carry a bigger payload and take a shorter route to another planet. This technique should be no more difficult than aerial refueling at jet speed, for no matter what speed is involved, two objects moving together at matched velocities have no speed relative to each other. Jockeying two spacecraft together certainly should be easier in one respect

—in space there is no air resistance, no wind, no bumpy air to disturb delicate maneuvers.

Timing is an especially critical factor in launching on interplanetary missions. The payload a given rocket can carry is very sensitive to the trajectory it will follow, and interplanetary trajectories change constantly as the planets move around the sun at different speeds.

There is a timetable for interplanetary travel. There are good years and bad years, good months and bad months, good days and bad days for starting trips. And, because of the constantly changing position of the launch pad as the earth rotates, good and bad times of day. There are "dead seasons" of interplanetary travel. When the earth and the target planet are passing each other on the same side of the sun, a direct trip between them would be impossible without unlimited power.

Not only must relative positions of the planets be considered, but their varying speeds as well. Mars, for instance, speeds up by 10,000 miles an hour at perihelion, an undesirable time to try to rendezvous with that planet. A better time is half a Martian year (343 earth days) later, when Mars is moving slowest in its orbit, other factors being favorable.

For spacecraft traveling via the minimum-energy routes, the most favorable launching dates for Mars include December 23, 1964; January 26, 1967; February 28, 1969. The best dates for Venus flights are March 28, 1964; October 27, 1965; June 5, 1967; January 11, 1969.

Like tardy taxpayers, we are penalized for launching late. A delay of a month, for example, can result in our having to add nearly 1,000 miles an hour to launch velocity.

For a trip to the moon, the timing problem is affected mainly by the earth's rotation. Daily, there is a period of about ten minutes that is best for starting lunar missions. As the earth turns, the aiming direction changes. In four minutes, it changes by one degree, and a one-degree error means a 4,000-mile miss. The fact that the moon's distance from the earth varies during a month is of only minor importance as far as lunar flight is concerned.

Launching toward another body in space is a problem of interception in space and time. A rocket must be launched in the right direction at the right time, and with the right velocity. This latter factor is especially important in launching space probes of the type which receive aiming and speed control only during the short powered phase of their journey. After engine burnout, such a spacecraft, being powerless, cannot correct any minor trajectory errors. Like a thrown rock, it is committed to following a ballistic path—a path that is determined by the rocket's direction and speed at the instant of thrust cutoff. Control of speed at cutoff is critical since an error of less than one mile per hour adds up enough over millions of miles to cause a spacecraft to miss its target by thousands of miles—more than 20,000 miles in the case of Mars.

The way around this problem is to equip a spaceship with *midcourse guidance*—a system which includes rockets that can be fired during or toward the end of the journey to make necessary trajectory corrections.

Adding to the problem of plotting space travel routes and guiding vehicles along them is the fact that there are no fixed routes in space. With all bodies in the solar system in constant motion at different speeds (except the "fixed" sun), no two trajectories are ever exactly the same, either in length or in the way in which they are affected by the various gravitational pulls involved. Moreover, there is no perfect mathematical solution for the motion of a vehicle in space as it is affected by all of the other bodies. The best science, with its finest tools, can do is to estimate trajectories. This involves estimating four separate numbers—launching speed, firing time, how far up, and how far left or right to

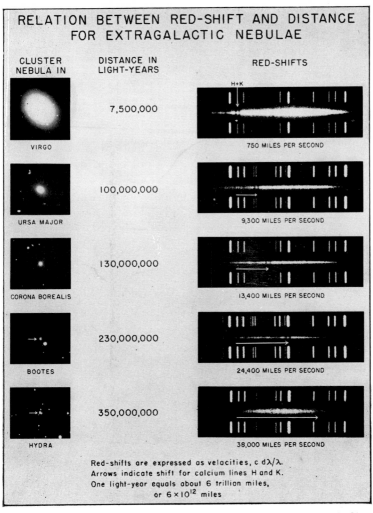

RELATION BETWEEN RED-SHIFT AND DISTANCE FOR EXTRAGALACTIC NEBULAE

CLUSTER NEBULA IN	DISTANCE IN LIGHT-YEARS	RED-SHIFTS
VIRGO	7,500,000	750 MILES PER SECOND
URSA MAJOR	100,000,000	9,300 MILES PER SECOND
CORONA BOREALIS	130,000,000	13,400 MILES PER SECOND
BOOTES	230,000,000	24,400 MILES PER SECOND
HYDRA	350,000,000	38,000 MILES PER SECOND

Red-shifts are expressed as velocities, $c \, d\lambda/\lambda$.
Arrows indicate shift for calcium lines H and K.
One light-year equals about 6 trillion miles,
or 6×10^{12} miles

Mt. Wilson—Palomar Observatories Photo

PLATE 1. Expansion of the universe is graphically illustrated in this series of direct and spectrum photographs showing how speed of recession increases with distance. Arrows on spectrum photographs of these galaxies indicate shift of their light toward red end of spectrum.

Mt. Wilson—Palomar Observatories Photo

PLATE 2. Cluster of galaxies indicated by pointer superimposed on photograph is the most distant group of galaxies identified with the 200-inch telescope. Cluster, located in constellation Boötes, is moving away at nearly half the speed of light.

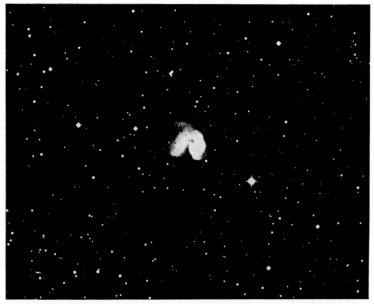

Mt. Wilson—Palomar Observatories Photo

PLATE 3. A possible collision of galaxies located in the constellation Corvus. Theory is that colliding galaxies pass through each other without collisions of their stars since the latter are so far apart. Interstellar gas clouds would collide, however, and gas thus excited may be the source of radio noise noted in some peculiar galaxies.

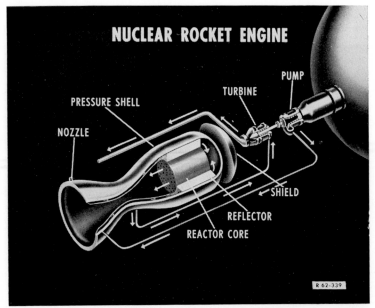

Plate 4. Nuclear rocket engine under development by Atomic Energy Commission and National Aeronautics and Space Administration. Main components are the reactor, consisting of the reactor core, a neutron reflector, and a pressure chamber; a nozzle to accelerate the propellant gas; and the turbopump, which pumps the hydrogen propellant from the spherical tank at upper right. Liquid hydrogen propellant flows through the reactor core, where it is heated and expelled through the jet nozzle.

Mt. Wilson—Palomar Observatories Photo

PLATE 5. The moon's dark sea areas will be investigated by unmanned explorer vehicles to determine best landing areas for the
Project Apollo mission. Light areas are literally riddled with craters,
and appear too inhospitable for first manned landing attempt.

NASA Photo

PLATE 6. *Gemini* spacecraft on display at McDonnell Aircraft, prime contractor. Craft weighs more than three tons. Unlike the *Mercury* capsule, the sixteen-foot escape tower will not be used. Ejection seats are built into the vehicle to provide crew with means of escape during launch or descent.

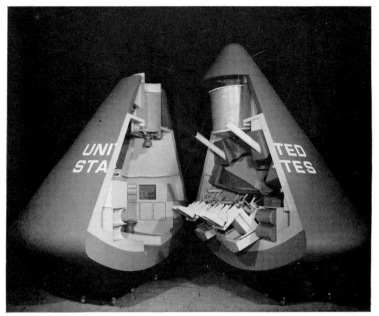

PLATE 7. Full-size engineering model of *Apollo* moon capsule built by North American Aviation. Three men will sit facing apex of the cone, as indicated by portions of seats visible in right half.

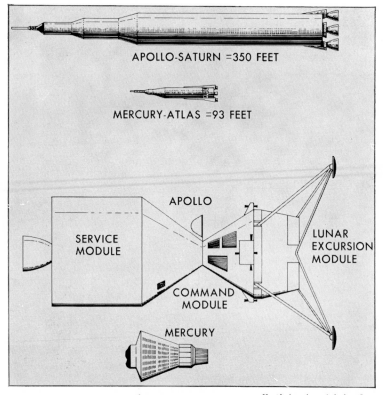

APOLLO-SATURN =350 FEET

MERCURY-ATLAS =93 FEET

APOLLO

SERVICE
MODULE

LUNAR
EXCURSION
MODULE

COMMAND
MODULE

MERCURY

North American Aviation, Inc.

PLATE 8. Drawings illustrating comparative sizes of projects Mercury and Apollo launch rockets and space vehicles. The *Apollo* capsule is shown with the lunar landing vehicle attached to its nose for transfer of the two crewmen who will descend to the moon, leaving the "mother ship" and one astronaut in lunar orbit.

PLATE 9. Artist's conception of the *Apollo* moon capsule in position for reentering the earth's atmosphere.

PLATE 10. Artist's conception of the *Apollo* moon capsule in orbit about the moon.

PLATE 11. Lunar landing area suggested by Clyde Tombaugh, Department of Astronomy, New Mexico College of Agriculture and Mechanic Arts, because of the variety of interesting features to study. Landing spot would be in the center of the white circle, which encompasses an area 200 miles in diameter. The gash at the right is known as the Alpine Valley. The large crater at the left of the circle is Aristotle. Tombaugh suggests that the radial markings around the crater might be spillings of lava. If so, they could contain natural tunnels offering ready-made living and laboratory accommodations.

Mt. Wilson—Palomar Observatories Photo

PLATE 12. Pocked lunar surface photographed in south central region. Large crater at bottom, near center, is Ptolemaeus, about 90 miles across. Crater Alphonsus is immediately above Ptolemaeus, appearing to share part of latter's upper wall, and is of particular interest since astronomers have noted possible gaseous discharges from tiny craters within it. Portion of Mare Nubium at right shows number of "ghost" craters.

Mt. Wilson—Palomar Observatories Photo

PLATE 13. Crater Clavius and surrounding region near southern edge of moon as photographed with the 200-inch telescope. Clavius is something over 100 miles in diameter. Note that craters have shadows at the right. Markings with bright side at right are mountains or hills.

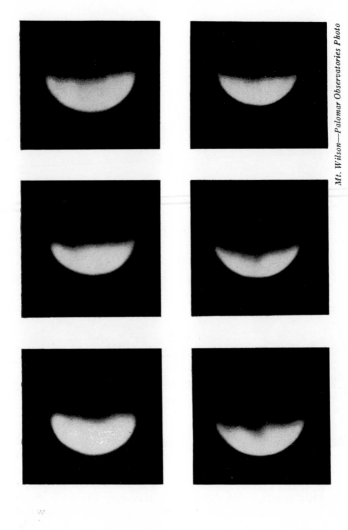

Mt. Wilson—Palomar Observatories Photo

PLATE 14. Venus. Views showing various phases of the planet, which hides its surface beneath an opaque atmosphere.

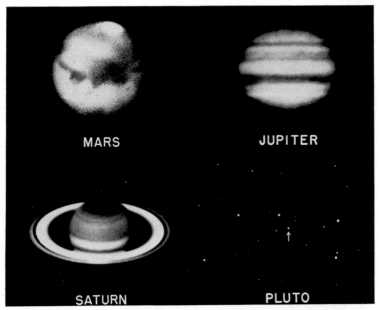

Mt. Wilson—Palomar Observatories Photo

PLATE 15. Mars, Jupiter, Saturn, and Pluto. Note polar cap on Mars. Pluto appears as mere point of light lost among the stars even in this photograph with the 200-inch telescope. Pictures do *not* show comparative sizes.

PLATE 16. Galaxies by the million spin like fiery cartwheels in space as far as the largest telescopes can see. This unusual group, displaying many different types, was photographed with the 200-inch telescope, looking toward the constellation Hercules.

aim—and then computing a trajectory on these estimates. If computation shows the trajectory is not close enough, new estimates are made and another trajectory computed from them.

What all this boils down to is that space travel would be impossible without high-speed computing machines. A report issued by California Institute of Technology's Jet Propulsion Laboratory during its supervision of a lunar probe mission illustrates the role the computer must play in any space mission, unmanned or manned:

> The speed at which the computer solves the trajectory problem is worth considering. In order to check the actual flight trajectory against the planned trajectory, the tracking stations report automatically by teletype the angle at which their antennas are aimed as they follow the probe. These teletyped messages are automatically converted into punched cards which are fed directly into the computer. The computer then proceeds to calculate eight separate trajectories, as well as all of the angles which would be seen on each of these trajectories at the various tracking stations. Automatically, then, the computer compares this set of trajectories with the actual measured angles and, on the basis of this comparison, it automatically searches the available data until it finds one single trajectory which most closely fits all of the observed data. It then computes all over again this new trajectory and sends back to the stations predictions as to what angles the stations should be observing at the next fifteen-minute interval. This entire operation, from the time the stations print their antenna readings on the teletype all the way through the computing and the time the prediction is sent back to the tracking stations takes about five minutes. The same calculation, carried out by hand, would require many years.

Manned spacecraft of the future will have to carry such computers on board.

VII. WHY GO INTO SPACE?

WHEN the United States announced that it would put a man-made satellite into orbit during the 1957-58 International Geophysical Year, the reason for going into space seemed plain and simple: Man was going to shoot instruments and eventually himself into the void because he is a curious and adventuresome creature.

It seemed then that all we had to do was settle back and be armchair spectators to "man's greatest adventure." But an easy enjoyment of the Space Age was not to be, for in October and November of 1957, Russia beat this country into space with the world's first two artificial satellites. The United States was unable to match the Russian success immediately. Its *Vanguard* satellite project, highly sophisticated and also highly publicized, was the victim of delay and failure. Even more embarrassing was our inability to match the payload weights the Russians were able to launch into orbit.*

This latter fact was the result of decisions made by the two countries some years earlier. Russia went ahead with development of the intercontinental ballistic missile at a

---

* Scientific payloads of *Sputniks I* and *II* weighed 184 and 1,120 pounds against 3.4 and 30 pounds for the first U.S. satellites.

time when nuclear bombs were very heavy and needed big rockets to carry them. The United States, on the other hand, didn't fix upon design of its first ICBM *(Atlas)* until a few years later, after much lighter, though no less effective, warheads were possible. The result was a U.S. intercontinental rocket with far less propulsive power than its Russian counterpart, and when the Space Age dawned this country could not begin to compete with Russia in lofting sheer weight into space.

Until October 4, 1957, many people had regarded Russia as rather backward in science and technology. But the first *Sputnik* reversed this idea, and immediately the reason, or reasons, for going into space seemed more complex: Congress and the public worried about America's scientific and technological status, and, therefore, political standing, in the eyes of a world being wooed and threatened by communism. Military men, fearing Russia might be first to develop a military capability in a new medium, predicted that, like air power, space power would mean control of the globe. They called for development of manned satellites, space stations, and a project to put Americans on the moon first.

Scientists were concerned, too, but more over American reaction than the Russian coup. By and large, they regarded space exploration as a strictly scientific undertaking and warned that "science must not be sacrificed" to political and military expediency, a syllogism that brought the scientific community to arms and won support from some of the highest political leaders. Many experts ridiculed suggestions that space exploration also involved immediate political, military, and economic ends. How, they argued, could the first exploratory satellites carrying some innocuous scientific instruments change the basic reason for going into space?

They were quite right, of course: *Sputnik I* and its successors didn't really change or create reasons for exploring space. The other reasons already existed in an age when scientific and technological prowess is synonymous with political, military, and economic strength. What the Soviet space feats *did* change, in time, was the minds of some people who had maintained there was no need to compete with Russia in space.

A year after the first Russian success, a new federal agency, the National Aeronautics and Space Administration, was established to plan and direct the civilian space effort. Since those early days many thinking people, including scientists, have come to recognize that the so-called space race is simply the latest round in the scientific and technological one-upmanship that has been going on since the beginning of mankind.

The fact that space exploration is a visionary undertaking doesn't mean that immediate and practical benefits aren't derived. To the rest of the world it is obvious that a nation able to hurl tons of hardware into space and guide a vehicle to photograph the back side of the moon certainly must have a scientific and technological potential. The psychological effect on the world is enormous, amounting, in fact, to both political and military pressure. The same sort of thing is true where economics are concerned. Russian sales of automobiles, bridges, and electronic equipment were reported to have increased in the world market following *Sputnik I.*

The House Committee on Science and Astronautics has reported: "To the extent that the welfare of the United States depends upon its stature in the eyes of the rest of the world, and to the extent that the scientific capability of the United States influences such stature, our space venture has a very marked practical utility. It may even mean the difference between freedom and dictatorship, between survival and oblivion." *

* *The Practical Values of Space Exploration,* House Report No. 1276, Report of the Committee on Science and Astronautics, House of Representatives, Eighty-seventh Congress, First Sess. (Rev., August, 1961), p. 20.

All of the foregoing, of course, is history. But an important part of it is still current history. For while the United States is committed to a multibillion-dollar space effort, including a manned trip to the moon with all possible haste, direction of the national space program is subject to debate and struggle between opposing philosophies. In the broad aspect, it is a struggle between science and technology. More specifically, it is a struggle between science and the military, science and politics, and science and public opinion since the military, politicians, and the public have either a more urgent need for technological achievement or are more impressed by it. The most serious disagreement over conduct of the space program is that between science and the military. If we are to believe leaders on both sides of the argument, either philosophy, given free rein, could lead to national disaster, or at the very least to second-rate status in space.

Two points should be made clear at this juncture: One is that by "military" we refer mainly to the military services, not to the Department of Defense, against which much of the military dissatisfaction is directed. From the services' point of view, DOD, which is, of course, under direction of civilians, has been too much influenced by scientific advisers, and, therefore, slow to acknowledge an urgent need for development, if possible, of a military capability in space.

The other is that the conflicts among groups involved in the space effort grow out of necessarily different philosophical approaches to the exploration and use of space, and as such are not to be condemned or criticized. Disagreement over direction of the space program, often between the experts within a given group, such as the scientists and technologists employed by NASA, is normal, healthy, and to be desired. But when narrow-minded specialists seek to place, or are allowed by their managers to place, their own special interests above national interests, failing to see the necessity for maintaining proper balance among the elements making

83

up the space effort, they or their managers are properly open to criticism.

There is an important third party to all of these debates: The layman voter and taxpayer, whose understanding, or lack of it, can affect national decisions of the most vital nature. In order to help him distinguish between "reasonable" and "unreasonable" space proposals, some scientists have suggested that all he need do is go to the "nearest high school physics teacher for the right answers." Regrettably, it is not as simple as that. The layman must also go to the professor of military strategy, the expert in mass psychology, the political science teacher, the foreign affairs specialist, the economist, the philosopher, and perhaps a few others as well. For what may be "right" as far as the physicist is concerned may not be the right decision for the statesman or military man.

There are some things, too, that only the layman himself can answer. It was that great body called the common man, not the experts, which answered, by its reactions, the question of *Sputnik I's* impact on world public opinion. Some of the highest scientific, technological, and political authorities grossly underestimated that impact. They argued (sometimes for obvious political reasons) that the real effect was of little import. And they argued against the idea of entering a space race with Russia. American public reaction was only crude emotionalism, they said, criticizing the press for whipping up sensational issues. But crude emotionalism or not, the U.S. layman properly reflected the impact upon peoples the world over, thus indicating the direction the space program was to take.

Yet in a very real sense today, the layman, and this includes most national political leaders, is perhaps more at the mercy of the expert than at any time in history. Too frequently, it seems, he must despair of either understanding what the experts are doing, or evaluating whether they are doing it properly. And when he hears that *they* cannot agree, one wonders whether he can be blamed for throwing up his hands and either abstaining from the decision-making or reaching his decisions on an emotional or purely political basis. It would be of some help if he had a program to the game so that he could at least properly identify the teams and their players and know something of their backgrounds and motives. But to a large extent even that is not available to him.

Unfortunately for the layman's understanding, the popular press rarely makes a distinction between space *scientists* and space *technologists*, usually lumping them together as "space scientists," and assuming that an expert called "doctor" must be a scientist even though the technologist may also bear that title. While both may be scientifically trained and certainly dependent upon each other for progress in the space program, their interests are not the same. In somewhat oversimplified terms, one is interested in scientific research, the other in engineering achievement. The scientist is interested in gathering information and knowledge from space. This may be information that is immediately useful, or it may be information that is so abstract and little understood that its immediate practical utility—and headline value—is practically nil. The technologist's need for information from space is vital, but he also seeks to apply it and to make practical use of the space medium in ways that are more likely to produce the engineering feat, the so-called space spectacular of high propaganda value.

But the press is not alone in failing to make this distinction. Even experts use the term scientist as a generic term for scientist and engineer.

How scientist and technologist differ and how this difference can produce real and serious disagreement over what should or should not be done in space has been illustrated by Dr. Eberhardt Rechtin, chief of the Telecommunications

Division of NASA's Jet Propulsion Laboratory: "Ask the individual in question what he thinks of the Mercury program. The scientist will invariably say that it is a terrible program. The technologist will almost always state that this program is advancing technology as rapidly as it possibly can and that, as such, it is a valuable and worthwhile program ... the few people in the Mercury program who believe that [it] is scientific in nature use a definition of science which is so broad as to include all of advanced technology." *

It is true that Project Mercury is of little scientific value. It is an engineering achievement involving development of new equipment and techniques—practical application—not discovery of new scientific knowledge in space.

As for the ultimate aims of the two, Dr. Rechtin puts it this way: "To the technologist there will always be high value in reaching the moon or the planets or the stars even if there were too little weight allowance to permit any scientific measurements to be made the first time. The technologist's point of view is only seldom understood by the scientist, who would maintain there is no point in having gone to your destination unless you can measure something while you are there." †

The conflict between scientist and technologist is complicated by money matters. Since the United States simply does not have unlimited monies to pump into space, the competition for funds is keen, and we often find the experts roundly criticizing the merit of each other's work. The scientist, whose information-gathering costs far less than, say, development of a manned satellite, is frequently of the opinion that the technologist is wasting a good deal of money trying to do things that could well afford to wait. He cries

---

* Eberhardt Rechtin, "What's the Use of Our Racing for Space?" An address before the Hughes Management Club, Los Angeles, Calif., July 14, 1960.
† *Ibid.*

for more basic research, from which flows knowledge fundamental to all things, whether they involve great technological achievements in space or the questions man seeks to answer about himself, life, and the universe. His fear of technological overemphasis has been expressed by Drs. L. V. Berkner and Hugh Odishaw in their book, *Science in Space,* which warns of a disease called "projectitis," a condition characterized by a "cancerous encroachment of technology over the sound objectives of space ventures." When vehicles command primary interest, they state, only secondary attention can be given to experiments in space.

But to those who dream of setting foot on the moon and other planets and to those who seek military developments in space, the vehicle is the thing.

Military technologists called for a space race from the launching of the first *Sputnik.* But many scientists were reluctant to admit that we had been forced into anything so childish as a space race, and a great body of them tried to stick by what they considered the loftier view, as expressed by Dr. Lee A. DuBridge, president of the California Institute of Technology: "The challenge of the Space Age is whether we use the great new technologies of space travel for peaceful and scientific purposes . . . or will we be led into wild programs of Buck Rogers stunts and pseudomilitary expeditions?"

Some scientists become self-appointed debunkers who ridiculed space proposals that did not serve strictly scientific purposes. The program to launch a man in a satellite was called a "stunt"; the proposal to send men to the moon was designed by "the space cadets." The fact that these programs now are part of the national space effort has by no means squelched these Space Age cracker-barrel philosophers.

Whether he is a debunker or not, the scientist often sees the military man as a starry-eyed science fiction devotee, and sometimes he is right. On the other hand, the military remembers those who scoffed at proposed development of the airplane as a major weapon. It also remembers that after World War II "some of our most respected scientists sold short the idea of developing long-range missiles. Impractical, they said; visionary. But six years after the United States went to work seriously on missiles, an operational ICBM with a 9,000-mile range was an accomplished fact." *

The military's unhappiness with the space program stems from the fact that the major effort, by presidential and Congressional decree, is oriented toward the *scientific* exploration of space, and is under direction of a civilian agency, NASA.

In terms of money, this translated in recent years to recommended budgets of $3.5 billion for NASA and $1.2 billion—excluding money strictly for missile procurement—for the Air Force, which receives 90 per cent of military space funding. In terms of programs, NASA is responsible for the majority of the most advanced space missions, including projects Mercury and Apollo, as well as unmanned exploration of the moon and planets. NASA and another civilian agency, the Atomic Energy Commission, are jointly responsible for development of high-thrust nuclear-powered rockets.

Military dissatisfaction goes all the way back to creation of NASA. The agency's predecessor was the National Advisory Committee for Aeronautics (NACA), a small research organization that conducted research and turned the results over to the military and other interested agencies.

In addition to absorbing functions of the old NACA organization, NASA acquired some of the most advanced programs then being conducted by the military. From the Navy it acquired Project Vanguard, with 158 scientists and engineers. From the Advanced Research Projects Agency (ARPA) of the Department of Defense it took over responsi-

* *The Practical Values of Space Exploration, op. cit.,* p. 20.

bility for some lunar probes and satellites, and from both ARPA and the Air Force it picked up the man-in-space program (which became Project Mercury) and development programs in the "super-thrust" propulsion field, including nuclear engines and a 1.5-million-pound-thrust rocket engine.

NASA also acquired certain military research and development facilities and personnel, including the Army's Jet Propulsion Laboratory, now directing the unmanned lunar and planetary exploration program, and the Army's space research team headed by the German expert, Dr. Wernher von Braun. At the time the transfers were made, by executive order, it was stated that the paramount objectives of the affected programs were of a nonmilitary nature.

The military, of course, shares in the benefits of NASA's activities. The National Aeronautics and Space Act of 1958, under which NASA was created, specifies that the civilian agency shall make available to defense agencies "discoveries that have military value or significance." Nevertheless, the military contends it is unrealistic to expect necessary military developments to spring from a civilian-directed effort. Many military men believe the participation of NASA and the military in the space program should be reversed or at least equalized to a fifty-fifty effort. Some think the spread and funding of NASA activities go a long way toward negating an important provision of the Space Act. That provision states that NASA will control all space activities except those "primarily associated" with research and development of weapons. But military men ask: "How do you separate what's scientific and what's military about development of manned satellites and advanced rocket engines?"

Recognizing that the distinction between military and nonmilitary activities cannot be precise, the Space Act also provides that the President of the United States will determine which agency—NASA or the Department of Defense —should be responsible for an activity in question. But military planners, looking over NASA's list of responsibilities, say this hasn't prevented an "imbalance" favoring science in the space program. By this they mean that the military-directed portion of the space effort has been largely restricted to reconnaissance, communications, and navigation satellites. The military has drawn up plans for more ambitious undertakings, including a manned satellite laboratory to research the military potential in space, but these programs have not received timely funding.

Considering the funding and scope of NASA activities, the military would seem to have a point in its complaint that too much of the space effort is scientifically oriented. But many thoughtful persons have wondered whether the complaint is justified. After all, there is the valid scientific argument that basic research can admit of no distinction between military and nonmilitary. What we have learned about the fundamental properties of the atom, for example, applies equally to bombs for destruction or lifesaving tools for medicine. The same thing applies to development of much basic equipment.

In view of this and the fact that NASA represents what may be the finest collection of scientific-engineering talent ever gathered into a single organization, isn't it feasible for the military to work with NASA, letting that agency conduct fundamental investigations and develop basic equipment while the military builds its special applications on that framework? Aren't the many and varied spacecraft NASA is using obtaining the right kinds of information for the military? Won't the project to send men to the moon require development of most of the basic things military craft would need?

In answer to these questions, the military contends that the scientist, unless working under military direction, cannot possibly have the sense of urgency the military requires. An Air Force general has put it this way: "A scientific experiment, although working under great pressure, can allow for delays for valid reasons. The military mission cannot."

The military sees a number of space missions becoming feasible for it over the next few years. These include ways to obtain more accurate maps of the earth's surface to improve the aim of ICBMs, new methods of warning against ICBM attack, and improved reconnaissance, navigation, weather forecasting, and communications.

Beyond these, the military thinks there are a number of *possibilities* that demand urgent investigation. These include a breakthrough in interception and destruction of ICBMs in space, manned orbital bombers, interception and inspection of unidentified satellites, discrimination of decoys from real ICBM warheads, and deployment of deterrent weapons in deep space as, perhaps in the future, the only way to insure their survival.

The Air Force, which has been assigned the job of prosecuting the military role in space, admits that the feasibility of such things is still questionable, but it contends we must investigate or run the risk that Russia may develop them first.

The Air Force is working with NASA in many of that agency's projects, including the manned lunar program. It has entered into formal working agreements with NASA and assigned its own specialists to duty with the civilian agency. And it has agreed with NASA that work of the agency and the military must be mutually supporting rather than competitive.

But while the Air Force says a significant amount of what it wants to find out and do in space will come out of NASA investigations, it points out there are many aspects of the space program that are "not common" to both the military and scientific efforts—"they are uniquely military and should be pressed by the military."

One item not common to both is the matter of man in

space. The decisions to proceed as soon as possible with manned orbital and lunar flights were political, not scientific, decisions which pained many scientists.

From the beginning, science has been unenthusiastic about putting man in space, and not without good *scientific* reason. Man is, at least in the current stage of space exploration, "an expensive nuisance" in the gathering of scientific information. He is in many ways less reliable, sensitive, and capable than instruments—instruments which must be sent along with him anyway and which do not ask to be brought back. The cost of putting man in space with all the equipment needed to keep him alive and return him safely far outweighs the value of the purely scientific data he can obtain. The successful manned satellite flights by both Russia and the United States have not changed this fact.

Dr. James A. Van Allen, discoverer of the radiation belts named for him, testified before the House Appropriations Committee that man will become superior to and more desirable than instruments when manned travel to the moon becomes possible. But this does not mean that science as a whole is in any great hurry to put man there. Indeed, there are some eminent scientists "who sincerely believe that manned space flight to the moon or to the planets is not worth the cost and that the money could be much better spent for more worthy purposes." *

This attitude, of course, has had a strong effect upon our scientifically oriented space program, bringing the complaint from the man-in-space proponents that "the great weight of scientific opinion that has influenced government decisions on space spending has for years favored instruments over man." †

As for man performing any military functions in space, a

* Richard V. Rhode, NASA, April 3, 1962.
† "Science Takes a Dim View of Man in Space," *Missiles & Rockets* magazine, May 29, 1961, p. 36.

favorite argument of the critics is that the role of pilot is even disappearing from modern aircraft, which can perform an entire mission automatically following takeoff by the pilot. In space, where maneuvers depend upon computation by complex equipment, it would appear that a man would have, in some ways, less to do as a pilot.

While admitting that it, too, has some reservations about the military jobs a man can do in space, the Air Force has maintained that it must not be restricted from exploratory developments merely because a clear application is not yet evident: "If we study war we find that it always has required that man's unique capabilities of reason, judgment, flexibility, and adaptability be used to the utmost." *

On the evidence so far it is clear, and the military concurs, that we cannot yet define any specific military space weapons. There are things the military would *like* to do, but whether they are feasible or pure Buck Rogers fantasy remains to be determined. And that, as far as the military is concerned, is precisely the point at the moment—there is a very definite reason for the military to go into space, and that is to investigate, to try to develop.

The military man does not trust NASA to do this for him as a by-product of the scientific space effort. His ultimate argument is that the scientist simply does not *think* like the military. What some scientists think of this argument was expressed to the author by a well-known and respected physicist in one four-letter word often used to express military thought. But the military has good historical reason for feeling thus, and Russian ICBM development is a case in point. As noted earlier, Russia started ICBM development five to six years ahead of the United States at a time when

* Maj. Gen. Marvin C. Demler, U.S. Air Force, Director of Advanced Technology, DCS/Research and Technology. From an address before the National Rocket Club Space Industry luncheon, Washington, D.C., March 15, 1962.

nuclear warheads still required very large rockets to boost them. We don't know the details of Soviet reasoning behind this decision, but there is no doubt that it was dictated by military thinking and military determination to push development despite the size of the warheads then available. The result was Soviet rockets with twice the thrust of our *Atlas* and *Titan* missiles.

This thrust gap is still hampering the U.S. space effort and will continue to do so for some time. Development of new rocket engines and spacecraft is a time-consuming business, so today's decisions affect our capabilities several years hence.

Despite military complaints about the scientific and peaceful emphasis of the space program, that emphasis, for good political reason alone, is not likely to change. The U.S. policy must remain as stated in the NASA charter, that space exploration is to be conducted for peaceful purposes "for the benefit of all mankind." As Dr. Edward C. Welsh, executive secretary of the National Space Council, put it: "All of our programs are peaceful. The Defense Department's activities are to maintain the peace; NASA's are to enable us to live better in peace." *

What should be done to better meet military needs, however, is to allow the military to proceed with development of its own programs in those areas not common to both space efforts. Some highly placed Defense Department spokesmen have proposed that this be done, but apparently there is divided opinion over the matter within the department.

After examining the issues that have arisen to complicate matters since October 4, 1957, we cannot help wondering sometimes whatever happened to our original reason for

* As quoted in "Space Council Unifying Goals," by James Baar, *Missiles & Rockets* magazine, January 8, 1962, p. 12.

going into space—the curiosity of man. And we cannot help joining the scientist in mourning the fact that it has become obscured by political and military considerations. Yet it will endure as the most basic motivation behind the drive for space; remove political and military motives and obviously, man still would seek in space the pure and simple satisfaction of his curiosity and spirit of adventure. But at the same time he would not proceed as quickly. There is no denying that we are going to set foot on the moon much sooner as a result of competition with Russia.

That motives other than curiosity should enter the space picture was inevitable. Historically, the development of new technologies, the conquering of new frontiers, becomes the business of many. In this connection, prosecution of the space program is equally the business of scientific and technological interests. The scientist must be allowed to conduct his basic research, and, if we are in a race, the technologist must be allowed to proceed with his applications as well as his investigations of military possibilities in a new medium.

Much has been said about other reasons for going into space, not yet mentioned here, including many "consumer benefits." The political and public relations spiels about the "new riches" expected to flow from space sometimes sound a bit like television commercials. However, there are some very real consumer products and benefits to come from space science and technology.

One of the most immediate advantages, already beginning to be realized, is that provided by weather satellites. The weather-watching, 285-pound *Tiros IV*, for example, gave several days' advance warning of Hurricane Carla in 1961, permitting thousands of persons to flee or otherwise prepare for what proved to be the potentially most destructive hurricane in years. The U.S. Weather Bureau estimates

95

that savings enabled by weather satellites soon will total hundreds of millions annually.

Tiros satellites, using television cameras, have transmitted thousands of useful cloud-cover photographs showing storms in early stages of formation. Other NASA weather satellite programs include *Nimbus* and *Aeros*. *Nimbus*, weighing about 650 pounds, is designed to operate in a polar orbit. A polar-orbiting satellite moves north-south around the earth, passing over the poles. With the globe spinning beneath it, such a satellite eventually views the world's entire surface.

Aeros is designed for operation in a 22,000-mile-high orbit where a satellite remains over one ground location. Three such satellites spaced at intervals of 120 degrees around the earth are able to provide continuous observation of weather on a global basis.

Another one of the most immediately attainable and widely useful benefits is the communications satellite. Industry estimates are that a single satellite costing $40 million can eliminate the need for laying an additional $500 million worth of transocean cables to meet the growing communications demand. Civilian communications satellite programs include the experimental *Echo* series. These are inflatable plastic spheres coated with highly reflective material. They are known as *passive* satellites since radio signals are merely bounced off their reflective surfaces. Radio signals won't curve around the earth, but they can be relayed around by bouncing them off an atmospheric layer or a satellite. The latter method is preferable because of uncertainties involved in atmospheric relay. To be really effective, such a system requires more than one satellite. One unique approach, known as Project West Ford, involves the placing in orbit of millions of tiny metal needles which spread out and form signal-reflecting bands around the earth.

The more advanced communications satellites are known as *active repeaters* since they are equipped to receive and

96

then retransmit signals to ground stations. Worldwide telephone and face-to-face television communication is possible with these satellites. Examples include NASA's *Relay, Syncom,* and *Telstar* projects. The *Syncom* satellite—synchronous-orbit communications—is designed for the "stationary" orbit, where its movement is synchronized with the earth's rotation. *Relay* is a 100-pound experimental repeater satellite, and *Telstar,* a 125-pound vehicle, is a joint project of NASA and the American Telephone and Telegraph Company.

The military need for satellite communications is critical. At present a system of ground and aircraft-borne relay stations is used to keep constant contact among U.S. forces scattered around the world.

Navigation satellites are another immediate space benefit. The Navy's *Transit,* which sends out a radio signal, already is helping guide ships at sea in all kinds of weather.

One of the most significant features of the space program is that its requirements stretch across the entire spectrum of science and industry. Thus, the largest list of useful developments are the "fallout" or indirect benefits, ranging from improved cooking pots to medical advances. Miniaturization of electronic instruments to measure physical responses of astronauts whirling in orbit has resulted in "electronic nurses" that continually monitor the condition of hospital patients; pressurized suits developed for space have enabled persons formerly bedridden with blood-pressure trouble to walk again; a sensor invented to check conditions inside rocket engines was adapted to check inside the human heart; a drug developed from a missile fuel is treating mental illness; and hearing has been restored for deaf persons by implantation of miniature electronic devices.

For the homemaker there are new utensils that survive an extreme temperature range because of research into rocket nose-cone materials, glass that remains sterile permanently, paints that never need renewing, and electronic stoves that heat coffee in a cup without making the cup hot. Out of experiments with algae, which may be used as food in space, has come a low-cost flour of high nutritive quality. Developments that have application in industry are numerous —new materials, processes, power sources, and tools, including rocket-flame equipment that is cutting mining costs and recovering ore previously unminable. High-speed computers developed out of missile and space technology are revolutionizing procedures and planning in business and commerce.

Among the future benefits predicted by space enthusiasts are laboratories on the moon to conduct low-gravity and high-vacuum research that is impossible on earth, a lunar sanitarium to remove heart-disease patients from the strain of earth's high gravity, use of natural resources of other planets, vacations on other planets, colonization of other planets to relieve earth's growing problem of overpopulation.

Such things obviously are going to take a while, and the more conservative experts feel some of them are just a bit far out, certainly not attainable in our time. Of these proposals, establishment of a lunar laboratory is the one that will be done first, certainly within the lifetimes of many persons today.

Of some philosophical interest is the question, "What will be the most valuable thing to come from the space program?"

A surprising number of the experts—scientists, statesmen, military men, lawyers, historians, sociologists, and psychologists—think the answer may be that space exploration will become a substitute for war. Several theories are advanced to support this idea. One is that space exploration could become such an expensive proposition that the United States and Russia eventually will have to forget enmities and pool their efforts if the larger goals are to be reached. There have been proposals from leaders of both nations for cooperation on some space projects.

An allied theory is that space research will become so costly that the two nations will be forced into thinking about reduced military spending. Still another suggestion is that the job of exploring space will become the "moral equivalent" of war by satisfying both psychological and material needs formerly sought in warmaking. And another is that Space Age destructive capability soon will reach the point, if it hasn't already, where war is unthinkable because no one could survive as the winner.

As far as presently envisioned space expense is concerned, it is estimated that the United States may spend up to $70 billion for its entire program, civilian and military, over the next decade. This is a huge sum, averaging $7 billion a year, or nearly $20 million a day. But as the National Space Council has noted, it is less than the $7.5 billion Americans annually spend on cigars and cigarettes.

VIII. SCIENCE IN SPACE

MAN may find his origins on the moon, for that presumably sterile world could hold the answers to the two most intriguing questions of space research: How was the solar system created? How did life begin?

While it may be that living things could not develop and flourish on so barren a place as the moon, analysis of its soil may enable us to trace the chemical beginnings of life. This belief is based on the fact that radiation from the sun and natural electrical discharges can cause formation of organic molecules from simpler inorganic molecules. The molecules thus created are not alive but are the more complex chemical compounds that are the basis of life. They have been produced artificially in the laboratory.

Creation of such prelife particles doesn't mean that life will develop wherever they are produced; other favorable conditions must be present, too, in order to make the still-unexplained transition from nonliving to living. But it supports the theory that life came about through a process of chemical evolution in which simpler molecules were joined into progressively more complex substances until life became possible. It also means that an important first step toward life can occur elsewhere, even on completely dead worlds where there is no likelihood of life itself ever developing. This shouldn't be surprising in view of the fact that nature often produces an overabundance of things, as if to insure greater chance for success in some undertaking.

Many scientists will be surprised if we do not find organic material on the moon. If it is found, it will lend credence to the theory that life can occur in many places throughout the universe. Further, lunar organic material might, because the moon's surface has remained undisturbed over the eons, include missing links which could explain the transition from nonliving to living. It is even suggested that low forms of life may exist on the moon, though most scientists doubt it.

The moon is believed to have been formed with the rest of the solar system about 4,500,000,000 years ago, and probably has changed little since. Thus, it may bear the original marks of creation and be able to tell us much more than the earth, where evidence of the days of formation has been obliterated by erosion.

The most commonly accepted theory concerning origin of the earth and moon is that they and the rest of the solar system condensed as separate bodies from a cloud of gas. Another is that most bodies of the solar system were built up by accumulation of cold chunks of matter such as meteoroids. A third idea is that the moon was whirled out of a fast-spinning and still-soft earth.

One indicator of the moon's origin would be seismic activity or "moonquakes." The occurrence of earthquakes is closely related to the flow of heat from the earth's molten interior. Detection of such disturbances on the moon could be evidence that it, too, has a fluid core, indicating that it formed as a separate molten body.

The strength of the moon's magnetic field could provide other clues. A strong field should be associated with the stirring of a fluid core. A weak field might indicate other things, including a solid core and formation by accretion of debris.

At the same time, it is conceivable that the moon might have both a weak magnetic field and a fluid core. If it is true that a body's magnetic field is generated by the stirring of its molten interior, the moon, which turns only once a month, would be a poor generator.

These things are open to investigation by robot vehicles designed to land on the moon. But ultimately man must go conduct such research himself, and that has become the primary goal of the nation's civilian space program under direction of the National Aeronautics and Space Administration.

Setting of this goal was, of course, dictated by political, not scientific, considerations, the aim being to place men on the moon ahead of Russia, or at least match any such Soviet feat. Only time will tell whether this will be accomplished. But whatever the outcome of the moon race, which may cost as much as $40 billion, one thing is certain: The U.S. space program has been given tremendous impetus by the decision to send men to the moon as soon as possible. Whereas exploration of space was proceeding on a piecemeal basis in various directions previously, establishment of a single major goal has quickened and united all facets of the program toward a common objective. As a focus of space activity, the lunar project will result in much earlier development of basic space capabilities that will have far-reaching implications for the entire space effort, military as well as civilian. As President Kennedy put it in setting the goal in mid-1961: "No single space project in this period will be more impressive to mankind, or more important for the long-range exploration of space."

Other space projects have been aligned to support the manned lunar mission—Project Apollo—to the fullest possible extent, for there are many things to be investigated and accomplished before man can venture a quarter of a million miles into space, land on an alien body, and return. In general, these fall into three categories: the environment in earth-moon space and on the moon as it affects spaceship design and man's safety, the performance of man in space, and development of spaceships and techniques of manned space flight.

One of the greatest hazards in manned space flight are giant solar flares of the type that fill interplanetary space with lethal streams of radiation in a matter of minutes. Only a relatively small percentage of solar flares—those which emit cosmic rays—pose a major threat. When such flares occur, an unprotected man in space or on the moon would receive a fatal radiation dose in minutes. The effects of these solar outbursts may continue in space for days, although the worst danger is during the first hour or so. The flare problem is being met in two ways: by study of flares with both earth and space-based instruments, tying into research aimed at devising reliable flare-prediction methods, and by development of materials and ways to shield astronauts.

The *Apollo* spacecraft will be able to turn around and speed home quickly in the event a really dangerous flare occurs or appears imminent.

Radiation also affects equipment, reducing performance of some electronic devices by more than half after several weeks of exposure.

Many satellites and space probes have investigated radiation from the very beginning of the space program. Among the later ones are OSO—Orbiting Solar Observatory—and IMP—Interplanetary Monitoring Probe. The OSO project, designed to study a broad range of solar phenomena, has recorded hundreds of solar flares, most of them relatively harmless, and will record hundreds more during the years immediately preceding manned flights to the moon.

Main purpose of the IMP satellites is to help develop better means of predicting the cosmic-ray type of flare. With such satellites measuring flares and magnetic fields in space while astronomers study the sun for certain visible flare indicators, improved prediction should result. Flare indicators visible on the sun's disc include sunspots and unusually bright patches associated with markings that reveal strong magnetic fields forming on the sun. Sunspot activity varies over a fairly predictable cycle, reaching a maximum every eleven years, at which time flares also reach maximum activity. But there are periods in between when flares also may occur.

At the moment, flare-prediction ability is such that four-day trips are the longest that can be made with fair confidence that no danger will be encountered. This is a somewhat shorter time than round trips to the moon will require.

The study and mapping of magnetic fields in space is related to the flare problem because radiation travels along magnetic lines of force. Studies show that when a flare occurs, a great tongue of charged particles, or *plasma*, also is shot into interplanetary space, sometimes enveloping the earth. The tongue drags with it magnetic lines of force originating on the sun. These lines form pathways along which radiation from subsequent flares is speeded from the sun, increasing the hazard.

Individual shielding appears to be the only feasible means of protecting men from flare radiation during space flights. Shielding for an entire three-man *Apollo* spacecraft would weigh about 3,500 pounds, according to one estimate, whereas individual protection at each astronaut's station—consisting of metal, plastic, glass, and perhaps a quilted blanket filled with water—would weigh only a third as much. Astronauts are not expected to remain under their shields at all times; solar observatories on earth will flash flare alarms, and spaceships will carry detection and warning equipment.

The Van Allen belts around the earth constitute an additional radiation danger, but one that can be minimized if spaceships pass through them quickly or use trajectories that carry them through the thinner portions of the belts near the polar regions. Project Mercury flights avoided the belts by remaining in low orbits.

The effects of space radiation, weightlessness, and high g loading on biological processes are being studied in such programs as BIOS, the Greek word for life, which to NASA means "Biological Investigation of Space." BIOS payloads, designed for recovery from both sounding rockets and satellites, carry human blood cells, bacteria that normally inhabit human intestines, mold spores, barley seed, grasshopper embryos, sea-urchin eggs, and single-celled creatures such as amoebae. These experiments include investigation of whether life is able to carry on normal feeding and cell division during long periods of weightlessness, how nerve tissue is affected by radiation, and whether weightlessness seriously affects photosynthesis in plants and fluid transport in animal tissue.

Of increasing importance as man ventures more frequently and farther into space is the matter of how much g loading biological processes can safely withstand, especially during reentry into the earth's atmosphere when a spacecraft is subjected to great deceleration forces as it slams into dense air. The earth's blanket of atmosphere presents both a problem and an advantage to returning spacecraft. The problem is that the vehicle cannot strike it at too high a speed or steep an angle, or deceleration will be so great the occupants will be squashed. The advantage is that the atmosphere can be used, first to slow a returning ship—atmospheric braking —and then to enable gentle lowering to earth by parachute or wing; otherwise, spaceships would have to make retrorocket descents all the way to the surface, as they must on the moon, and, therefore, carry additional rocket equipment and fuel into space.

Astronauts returning in America's first manned spacecraft, the bell-shaped, 2,400-pound *Mercury* capsule, underwent 7½ g's—7½ times the force of earth's gravity—as the atmosphere slowed the vehicle from orbital velocity to 270 miles an hour in a little over five minutes. The problem of reentry is magnified when a spacecraft is returning from the moon rather than from an orbit about the earth, for the laws of space travel are such that a freely falling body returning from space arrives at the same velocity that it needed to depart from the earth in the first place. In the case of return from the moon this is equal to escape velocity of 25,000 miles an hour. In the case of return from other planets, the return velocity may run much higher.

Going hand in hand with the g-loading problem and also increasing with speed is heating of the spaceship by atmospheric friction. A vehicle which reenters too fast will burn up like a meteor. Even entry at "safe" speeds requires protection of the craft by a heat shield, which on the *Mercury* capsule is a glass-resin material on the blunt end. Temperature of this shield rises to 3,000 degrees F. as it vaporizes to carry away 99 per cent of the heat generated.

Together, deceleration forces and heating pose a difficult guidance problem for spaceships returning from the moon. Unlike the *Mercury* capsule, the returning lunar vehicle does not begin reentry from orbit, thus facing greater difficulty in establishing and maintaining the required shallow reentry angle. In order to decelerate from 25,000 miles an hour and land safely on its first pass around the globe, the lunar craft must approach the earth on a trajectory that just grazes the atmosphere, then very gradually settles lower while making nearly a complete circuit of the earth.

Taking the most extreme case—a simple capsule with no wings or flat surfaces with which to provide aerodynamic lift and control when it hits the atmosphere—the returning vehicle would have to reenter no more than 3½ miles above the proper trajectory. Otherwise, it would skip out into space again, perhaps to escape or orbit indefinitely. If the capsule undershot the trajectory by more than 3½ miles, entering the denser atmosphere too soon, its occupants would be killed by crushing deceleration or heat.

The limits described constitute a critical, seven-mile *reentry corridor* which the capsule must hit and stay within during atmospheric braking. Width of the corridor can be extended to forty miles if the capsule's design allows it to achieve some aerodynamic lift. *Apollo*'s design will permit this, and it will control its attitude, or angle of attack, by use of small reaction jets located on its surface.

But why not give the craft a rocket engine with which to slow down or kick itself into a low orbit before starting reentry? This could be done but it would add great weight and complication to the final stage of the moon rocket. The *Mercury* capsules must use retro-rockets to initiate return from orbit. But since this requires subtraction of only a little speed—about 350 miles an hour—only small rockets are needed.

Even a forty-mile reentry corridor presents a very difficult guidance and control problem, pointing up the importance of continuing research to determine man's natural g force limitations. Once these are established, techniques may be developed to enable him to withstand more g force and thereby provide an extra margin of safety. Such research may also lead to development of ways to make emergency escapes into the earth's atmosphere from orbiting or returning spacecraft. An escape capsule making a direct reentry would subject its occupants to 350 g's. Small monkeys riding in a whirling centrifuge have sustained up to 400 g's even without a form-fitting couch for support. Man has withstood as much as eighty g's, but only for seconds.

Experiments have subjected biological payloads up to eighty g's on reentry. Programs contributing to this research include the X-15 and projects known as Scout, Fire, and Trailblazer. Some experiments involve rockets which shoot high into space and then propel payloads back down into the atmosphere at high speeds that simulate return from the moon.

Yet another reentry problem is that of communication with returning spacecraft. Changes in the heated atmosphere surrounding a reentering vehicle cause radio communications blackout for a short time, as if radio waves could not pass through the layer of hot gas around the craft. This lack of communication, although expected, has caused some uncomfortable moments during recovery of astronauts from orbit. In the case of a spacecraft which uses aerodynamic lift during reentry, the period of communications blackout may be far longer than for the *Mercury* capsule, which drops back to earth fairly quickly. The matter is under investigation in several projects, including a reentry study designated RAM—Radio Attenuation Measurement.

Science also is investigating space to learn the danger from meteoroids and micrometeoroids.* Some research vehicles count the particles by telemetering signals to the ground when objects strike their skin. Before man ventures on long space journeys, he wants to know several things about these objects: What is their range in size? How numerous are they? How fast do they travel? What is their effect on materials?

The chances of a spaceship colliding with an object big enough to wreck it are very, very slim—there just aren't many meteoroids that big. Even tiny objects possess considerable penetrating power at high speed. However, research indicates spaceships need only a thin extra outer skin, or "meteor bumper," to protect them from the ordinary particles. Experiments in which one-eighth inch pellets have been shot with near-satellite speed at two one-sixteenth inch aluminum sheets placed an inch apart show the first sheet dissipates

* In space, they are "oids," as distinguished from objects which enter the atmosphere or reach the earth's surface.

most of the impact, with only slight penetration of the second sheet. Of course, spaceships are made of harder metals than aluminum.

Extending investigations of space to the moon and paving the way for landing of manned expeditions are projects designed to examine and map the moon with robot devices. These include *Ranger, Surveyor,* and *Prospector. Ranger* is a series of "hard" landing spacecraft running at least 675 pounds in weight and carrying seismometers, television cameras, radiation counters, and other instruments. The equipment, contained in a metal sphere floating in fluid and surrounded by balsa wood, can survive impacts of 150 miles an hour and radio lunar data to earth for a month.

The more advanced *Surveyor,* weighing about 750 pounds, is equipped with retro-rockets to land it gently on the moon. Instruments include more television cameras, a drill to probe five feet into the lunar crust and analyze its composition, a seismometer, and devices to check radioactivity, day and night temperatures, and for any trace of lunar atmosphere. Five of the dozen *Surveyors* are designed to enter an orbit about the moon for TV scanning and investigation of possible landing sites.

Prospector, as originally planned, involved the most thorough lunar investigation possible without the presence of man, including mobile vehicles to explore the surface by remote control from earth and a mission to bring back samples of moon soil. However, with man aiming to visit the moon as soon as possible himself, the need for *Prospector* has been questioned.

In addition to their exploring activities, the lunar robots serve as vehicles for development and test of much basic equipment required for manned vehicles.

The unmanned explorers are directed at certain "optimum aiming areas" on the moon. All of these areas are on the side of the moon facing the earth, and all are on the left side of the moon's face (the moon's own right) as we see it with the naked eye or binoculars.* (Plate 5.) Several reasons dictate the choice of landing areas. For one thing, it is impossible to communicate directly with craft landed on the unseen back side of the moon. For another, it is desirable to have the vehicles land on the relatively smooth, flat plains of the moon—the maria—and the left portion contains more of such terrain. There also are trajectory and timing requirements so scientists tracking the vehicles are able to maintain contact with them during final approach and landing.

Some *Rangers* are programmed to approach impact on a vertical descent which is advantageous for surface photography. They aim for a relatively small area roughly 100 miles in diameter in the middle of the left side of the moon. This location is in a large maria known as the Ocean of Storms—on a lunar map about fifty miles northeast of the small crater Euclides and eighty miles from the Riphaeus mountains. Other *Rangers* extend this area to a huge oval measuring more than 500 by 1,300 miles. The *Surveyors* explore a still wider area, extending landings to almost the entire left half of the moon.

Two of the most important objectives of the unmanned lunar program are collection of information affecting design of the manned landing craft and selection of a landing site for *Apollo*. Things under investigation include the moon's surface hardness, whether it has deep layers of dust, whether its plains contain cracks, pits, and rubble that would endanger a manned landing. Through the most powerful telescopes the lunar plains appear quite smooth, but the instruments cannot discern objects less than several hundred feet across.

A feature of the lunar surface which has led to widely

* Not with telescopes, since they invert the moon's image.

divergent theories is its dust. There is little doubt that there is a layer of dust since measurements during a lunar eclipse show the moon's surface cools off very quickly as the earth's shadow moves across it, much more quickly than the earth's rocks give up stored heat. This indicates a material of low thermal conductivity, one which conducts heat to only a small depth. Only fine dust fits this picture.

How thick is the moon dust? Scientific thought is divided into two main camps: Some experts think the dust reaches depths of hundreds of feet, and is soft and yielding, in which case spaceships would be swallowed by the moon. Others believe the dust may be at most only an inch or so deep. This theory is supported by radio telescopes which observe radio waves that penetrate the dust layer. These observations are by no means conclusive, however.

The amount of meteoritic dust falling on the earth has been used in attempts to estimate thickness of lunar dust. According to one estimate, the moon collects dust at the rate of three feet every 1,000,000,000 years. If this is so, the moon should have accumulated enough dust for a layer fifteen feet thick. Of course this is only guesswork. And even if it is correct, distribution of this dust over the entire lunar surface is still another matter. Gravity, in combination with other effects, would tend to move it into lower areas.

There are at least two schools of thought on whether the dust, even if thick, would pose a problem for explorers. One school thinks the dust particles would be charged by bombardment of solar radiation, thereby acquiring an electrostatic charge which would cause them to repel each other. In this case the dust layer would be in a state of suspension, therefore loose and unable to support a spacecraft. The other school rejects this idea, holding that in the almost perfect vacuum on the moon, dust particles would be compacted into an unyielding surface. Experiments in which objects have been dropped onto dust in vacuum chambers confirm this idea.

Only landings of spacecraft at various places on the moon will determine which of these theories is correct, if, indeed, either is entirely right. Although the moon is usually described as having no atmosphere, it may very well have a quite tenuous atmospheric layer created by gases escaping from the crust. If this is true, perhaps the lunar dust would be loose, at least during gaseous outflow. It has been suggested, in fact, that the dust may at times flow across the surface like water. This idea is based on the theory that the moon dust actually is volcanic ash. If volcanic activity is or was present, there could be today sporadic eruption of gas from spots on the moon's surface. There have been indications of this recently, in fact. This would present the same situation that exists in some volcanic areas on the earth: The upward flow of gas lifts the fine ash, "fluidizing" it so that it spreads like a liquid. Such flows have reached speeds of sixty miles an hour.

Yet another idea concerning the dust is that the impact of cosmic rays and other radiation on the moon would "sputter off" bits of material which would act to cement surface particles into a crust that would support weight.

The manned space program is proceeding concurrently with the unmanned exploration of space and the moon. In it, man is finding out how to survive and work in space, how to build spaceships that permit this, and how to fly them.

From one point of view, the potentially weakest link in manned space flight is man himself. Largely out of his element in atmospheric flight, he is literally out of his world in space flight, having to take along and maintain a totally artificial environment, eat, sleep, think, and react in a state of weightlessness, and face travel problems that only high-speed computers can solve.

The first big goal of manned space flight has been to demonstrate that man can be placed in space, sustained there, and returned safely. With this accomplished by manned orbital missions, the next step is determination of how well man can perform in space, whether he can play a vital role in control of the spacecraft rather than be restricted to the status of mere passenger.

The *Mercury* capsule was designed primarily to solve the first problem, being capable of completely automatic operation from beginning to end so that no matter what happened to the astronaut, he could be returned safely. But the capsule also was equipped with a manual as well as an automatic control system, allowing the pilot to take over partial or complete control for such critical things as control of capsule attitude in orbit, firing of retro-rockets, control of attitude during retro-rocket firing in order to reenter at the proper angle, control of natural wobbling of the spacecraft during reentry, and bringing of the capsule back to stable flight if it started tumbling. Thus, the *Mercury* craft, controlled in space by short bursts of gas from eighteen nozzles located on its surface, permitted the first test of man's ability to function as a space pilot, and the result was gratifying beyond all expectations. The very first American astronaut to make an orbital flight, Col. John Glenn, reported that had he not been aboard the capsule on that particular flight, it might not have been able to return to earth. Due to malfunctioning of the automatic control system while in orbit, he was largely in control of the ship himself through the end of the flight.

Though the *Mercury* flights rank as achievements of the first magnitude in the history of manned space flight, a more conventional craft, the X-15, is credited with a feat of equal importance—the world's first round trip into space with a winged "aerospace plane." Air Force Maj. Robert M. White flew the rocket-powered ship to a height of more than fifty-nine miles a few months after the Marine colonel's success. White's speed was far short of orbital velocity, but he won astronaut's wings since fifty miles has been set as the minimum altitude required for astronaut's rating.

There are two good reasons why we seek to achieve as much man-control of spaceships as possible. One is that it means greater chance for mission success, for automatic equipment can fail. The other is that with a man able to take over as pilot, spacecraft require considerably less automation and less complication. This does not mean that automatic controls can be eliminated; man and machine must complement each other for highest reliability.

The next most advanced vehicle in the manned program is the two-man *Gemini* series. (Plate 6.) These dozen ships serve as both laboratories and training craft, subjecting men to progressively longer periods in earth orbit. *Gemini* is basically an enlarged version of the *Mercury* capsule, weighing two to three times as much, depending upon the mission involved, and permitting two astronauts to ride side-by-side. *Gemini's* primary purpose is development of techniques enabling manned ships to rendezvous with and attach themselves to other spacecraft in orbit. Rendezvous with an orbiting tanker is one way of carrying out a flight to the moon, allowing a spaceship to replenish the fuel it used in escaping the main pull of earth's gravity. Orbital rendezvous also can be useful at the moon.

In the *Gemini* rendezvous operation, the tanker ship, a 1,700-pound *Agena* satellite, is lofted into a circular orbit 150 miles high, and tracking stations determine its orbit. The manned craft then is fired into an elliptical orbit that is slightly lower but which has an apogee of 150 miles, placing it at intervals into the same orbit as the tanker. In the lower orbit, *Gemini* naturally travels a bit faster than the tanker, enabling it gradually to overtake the *Agena* as both coast

114

in orbit without power. This eliminates the necessity of bringing the two vehicles together by a direct ascent which requires a difficult split-second launch of the second ship.

Ideally, *Gemini* comes within twenty miles of the tanker before the astronauts use propulsion units to guide their ship on final approach, using both radar and visual observation for the "docking" maneuver, in which a two-foot cone extending from *Gemini*'s nose hooks into the target rocket. The spacecraft separate before *Gemini* returns from orbit following the practice rendezvous.

Gemini can sustain two men in orbit for a week or more, providing various tests of men and equipment. By the time the first *Apollo* spacecraft is ready for test and training missions, much more will be known of man's reaction to extended periods of weightlessness. Short periods have no ill effect, in fact produce a feeling of exhilaration. But on longer flights it can result in the space equivalent of seasickness. Other effects of weightlessness include reduction of man's tolerance to stress, *g* force, and temperature. These things can be combated by rotating the ship to produce artificial gravity, but it is desirable to avoid this since it adds weight and complication to spacecraft.

Also to be guarded against in space flight is the so-called breakoff phenomenon or feeling of detachment experienced even in atmospheric flight at high altitudes. This is the result of isolation and what psychologists call "sensory deprivation," meaning the absence of sights, sounds, smells, etc., which man's senses are used to receiving, sometimes leading to hallucinations. Experts think these things may be counteracted by giving astronauts familiar surroundings, for instance painting spacecraft interiors in colors to suggest the earth environment—ceilings blue, floors brown. This might have a secondary use in helping spacemen adjust to long periods of weightlessness when there is no real "up" or "down" in their vehicle. In general, every effort is being made to provide man with his own natural living conditions in space, including a "shirtsleeves" environment so he doesn't have to remain in his spacesuit at all times.

The climactic phase of the U.S. manned lunar exploration program begins with test and training flights of the vehicle that will take three men to the moon and back. As currently planned by NASA, the basic *Apollo* spacecraft consists of three thirteen-foot diameter "building-block" sections. The forward section is the crew capsule, which in outward appearance is simply a huge, smoothly rounded nose cone several times the size of the *Mercury* craft. (Plate 7.) Crew members sit side by side facing the apex of the cone. Attached to the base of the cone is the so-called service section, a cylinder somewhat longer and heavier and containing small propulsion units for guidance correction and rockets for the return trip. The third section is an excursion vehicle equipped with lunar landing rockets.

This entire assemblage sits atop the booster rocket that is used to hurl it into space. *Apollo*'s first missions are restricted to earth orbit while men and machines are trained and tested. For these flights the spaceship is boosted from earth by an eighteen-story, two-stage *Saturn* rocket.

For flights to the moon, *Apollo* will be boosted by a three-stage rocket known as the *Advanced Saturn*. The first stage of this rocket consists of a cluster of five engines, producing a total of 7,500,000 pounds of lift-off thrust. The second stage is powered by five smaller engines developing 1,000,000 pounds total thrust, and the third has one engine providing 200,000 pounds of push. Together, the spacecraft and its booster tower more than thirty-two stories above the launch pad. (Plate 8.)

Although the *Advanced Saturn* is a most powerful rocket, it still is not capable of sending *directly* to the moon a three-man spaceship containing all of the equipment, supplies, and fuel needed to land on the moon and then return. This means that the mission must be accomplished in steps. NASA has proposed several ways of doing this. One is to place the entire *Apollo* spaceship in orbit about the earth and then fuel it before it proceeds to the moon. This requires at least two *Advanced Saturns*—one to loft a tanker into orbit, and another to send *Apollo* up to meet it. Following the fueling operation, the spaceship pulls out of orbit for the trip to the moon. At the moon it uses braking rockets to decelerate and then touchdown rockets to lower it gently to the surface. On the return trip, two sections of the spaceship take off from the moon, leaving the third behind after using it as a built-in launch pad.

Obviously, another way to solve the problem is simply to cut down the size of the spacecraft that is to be landed on the moon. This can be done by sending fewer men to the moon—or by sending three astronauts but permitting only two to land. This latter method is the one currently given major planning emphasis by NASA as the most desirable in terms of cost, time, and chance for safe landing and takeoff at the moon. Its main advantage is the fuel and weight saving involved. Instead of lowering an entire three-section spacecraft weighing more than fifty tons to the moon, only one section, a lunar excursion "bug" weighing much less need be landed. The bug doesn't have to carry all of the equipment, supplies, and fuel for the trip home, so it can use less powerful rockets and less fuel. The rest of the spaceship, tended by one astronaut, remains in orbit 50-100 miles above the moon. Following exploration of up to four days, the two astronauts use the landing craft to ascend from the moon. They rendezvous with the orbiting mother ship, reattach their bug to it and transfer back into the crew capsule. The bug is jettisoned and the two remaining sections head homeward. Just before reentering the atmosphere, the now useless service section is jettisoned and the crew capsule reenters and lands by parachute. (Plate 9.)

The fuel and weight saving in the lunar orbit rendezvous method—known simply as LOR—cuts the size of the *Apollo* spacecraft enough to permit a single *Advanced Saturn* to launch it in a *direct* trajectory to the moon. The earth orbit step is eliminated in favor of a lunar orbit rendezvous which requires no refueling. Since the moon's gravitational pull is only one-sixth that of the earth's, a relatively small vehicle can accomplish landing and takeoff from the moon with its own rockets.

The saving in time is not in travel to the moon, which in either case takes about 2½ days. It is in the time required to develop and flight test the heavier and more complicated equipment needed to decelerate and then soft-land the entire three-man *Apollo* spacecraft on the lunar surface. Development of the smaller excursion bug should require less time, perhaps speeding the landing of men by a year. Overall, NASA estimates savings of 10 to 15 per cent in cost over the earth rendezvous method of reaching the moon.

A number of experts feel that chances for safe return of the expedition are increased by not risking the entire earth-return vehicle in a lunar landing. Added safety during the landing operation should result from the fact that the excursion bug is smaller, more compact, less complicated, and, therefore, less likely to receive a damaging jolt during touch-down. Another safety factor cited by those who favor LOR is the much lower speed required for the rendezvous operation: Orbital velocity about the moon is only some 3,400 miles an hour, compared with nearly 18,000 miles per hour about the earth. Launching of the bug to meet the mother ship is, therefore, less critical as far as timing is concerned.

Use of the LOR approach requires a three-section *Apollo* spacecraft thirteen feet in diameter, fifty-five feet long, and weighing about forty-three tons. (Plate 10.) The conical crew capsule is twelve feet long and weighs five tons. The service section is a twenty-three-foot long, twenty-three-ton cylinder equipped with a 20,000-pound-thrust engine for the return trip. The two-man lunar lander is twenty feet long and weighs fifteen tons.

Although NASA planning emphasizes the LOR type of mission, the space agency is not definitely committed to it. Design of the basic *Apollo* spacecraft and its booster rocket is such that the various pieces and stages are adaptable to other methods. NASA is continuing study of other possibilities, including a smaller *Apollo* spacecraft designed for only two men. The earth-rendezvous technique would be used, and the entire three-section ship would be landed on the moon, eliminating the need for lunar rendezvous. This method might be used if continuing studies and experience show that lunar rendezvous would be a marginal operation as far as safety of the astronauts is concerned. There are experts who think it would be too risky. If something goes wrong during a rendezvous in orbit about the earth, astronauts undoubtedly can reenter the atmosphere and return to earth safely. But if something goes wrong during a rendezvous operation about the moon, chances of the astronauts returning safely seem smaller. The moon has no atmosphere to permit gentle landing by parachute.

There is yet another possibility if all other methods appear too risky. This would be a direct, three-man flight using a bigger booster rocket known as the *Nova*. With a weight-lifting ability two to three times that of the *Advanced Saturn*, *Nova* not only would eliminate rendezvous but would improve chances for mission success. *Nova* would be used, however, only if all else failed—that is, if continuing manned flights in earth orbit show that rendezvous is too difficult, or if other serious problems arise. If the United States is forced to fall back on *Nova*, the moon expedition would be delayed several years, for this booster is in a much earlier stage of development than the *Advanced Saturn*. In all probability, the moon race would be lost to Russia.

Whatever route *Apollo* takes to the moon, astronauts will receive a great deal of training in space before the actual moon landing is attempted. The first moon trip probably will involve only a flight around the moon and back to earth. The first explorers on the moon will be space veterans who have studied the moon thoroughly from orbit before attempting a descent.

With regard to the moon race, there are rocket men who feel that the United States will be extremely lucky to land men on the moon ahead of Russia. The fact that NASA has changed its plans for the expedition—selecting an approach that not a few experts consider marginal—is evidence that the space agency is trying to shave off time wherever possible.

NASA's earlier plan for the moon trip, calling for use of orbital refueling about the earth, was selected instead of a direct, *Nova*-type flight because the smaller *Advanced Saturn* booster would be available much sooner. The plan for this was formed after President Kennedy called for a speedup of the effort in mid-1961. At that time the target date for the expedition was no later than 1970, with the possibility that it might be accomplished a year or so earlier. The official estimate was that the United States had a fifty-fifty chance of beating Russia. The change to the LOR method raised the possibility that the trip could be made in 1967-68, presumably changing the odds in our favor, although NASA has made no optimistic public statements.

Despite NASA's efforts to find means to speed the *Apollo* program, there are critics who say it still isn't proceeding as quickly as it could. Development and test of spacecraft and booster could be speeded, according to them. Critics include those who say a large solid-fueled rocket booster—big enough to provide the first mighty thrust toward the moon—could be developed to the flyable stage faster than big liquid rockets. Solid rockets, which have advanced considerably in recent years, are very much simpler in construction and operation. NASA is exploring the possibility of using a solid booster, but, according to the critics, not with enough effort.

Russia has revealed few details of its manned lunar program. However, Russian scientific papers have indicated that the Soviets may be planning a moon trip no later than 1965 because solar flare activity will be at a minimum between July, 1964, and July, 1965. Russian scientists are reported to be recommending that the 1966-70 period is unsafe for lunar expeditions.

In order to give the United States the greatest possible chance to beat Russia to the moon, a daring plan has been suggested—a one-man, one-way trip.* Under this plan, which could speed manned landing by two years, unmanned cargo rockets would put food, supplies, and equipment at a preselected site on the moon. The lone astronaut then would be landed and spend perhaps up to three years on the moon before he could be picked up by an *Apollo* ship. According to studies, he could be supplied by cargo rockets, survive indefinitely, and perform useful scientific work, perhaps helping prepare for the landing of *Apollo*. During his stay on the moon, the astronaut would be in constant radio contact with earth. If it were deemed necessary, a companion astronaut could be sent to join him in another one-way capsule.

A great deal of thought and study is being devoted to selection of a landing site for the *Apollo* expedition. (Plate 11.) Safety is the primary consideration. Ideally, the first men to

---

* John M. Cord and Leonard M. Seale, Bell Aerosystems Co., from their presentation entitled "The One-Way Manned Space Mission," before the Institute of the Aerospace Sciences National Summer Meeting, Los Angeles, Calif., June 19, 1962.

land on the moon will be almost as familiar with the touchdown spot as they are with their own backyards as a result of information from closeup, three-dimensional, color television photos. The landing will occur in a maria (if dust is no problem), hopefully near a crater that will provide more varied information about the moon than a relatively featureless plain. The first landing probably will be near the equator.

For later explorations, there have been strong recommendations that the moon's polar regions would be the most fruitful for scientific investigation because they contain areas that are in eternal darkness. Such regions exist because sunlight strikes the polar areas at such a slant that mountains and crater rims cast long shadows. Since the position of the polar regions is changed but little by the moon's rotation, some parts, such as crater floors, never can be lighted, and it is in just such areas that water, if it exists on the moon's surface, might be found in the form of ice. Organic compounds and certain minerals which decompose under heat and radiation might also be found in such regions.

More importantly, a number of experts believe such "twilight" areas could harbor some low form of life, perhaps something akin to the anaerobic bacteria, which require no free oxygen. While it is generally believed that the moon probably has no life, the idea is not entirely ruled out. On the unprotected portions of the moon's surface, life would be killed by heat and radiation. But it might be able to survive and even flourish in protected shadow areas or perhaps several feet below the baked lunar surface if small amounts of water were present.

The possibility that organic molecules may exist on the moon, to say nothing of life, has resulted in a stringent NASA rule requiring sterilization of spacecraft. Even one bacterium, if landed in a location where it could survive, might multiply so quickly that its descendants would spread over

122

an extremely wide area in a very short time. If this happened, we would be unable to tell whether organic material or life discovered on the moon had originated there or on earth.

At the same time, it has been suggested that discovery of organic material or life on the moon may not prove anything with regard to origin anyway. This idea is based on the theory that in the past the earth suffered collisions with bodies large enough to knock some of its material into space, sending it as far as the moon. Once knocked into earth-moon space, it is conceivable that earth dust containing organic molecules or microscopic life could be spread even farther, perhaps to other planets. According to an old theory known as the *panspermia* hypothesis, life spores may be spread through the universe by the pressure of sunlight, or, perhaps, via meteoroids. Many scientists discredit the panspermia idea, holding that radiation in space would kill such germ spores. But others think the spores could be carried in chunks of meteoroid material large enough to protect them. Meteorites have indeed been found to contain organic substances, and material from them even has produced growth of bacteria in test tubes. But it is impossible as yet to state whether the meteorites brought these things from space. Meteorites are porous and begin absorbing organic substances and bacteria from the air the moment they enter the earth's atmosphere.

The layman at this point may very well pose his own theory—that the seeds of endless controversy may exist regardless of what is found on the moon or elsewhere.

Many other questions about the moon should be more easily settled once man follows the robots there to conduct thorough study. On-the-spot seismic investigation should reveal whether the moon has a molten core. As mentioned earlier, the answer to this question bears on the origin of the moon, and, perhaps, the earth. If no moonquakes are detected, we would suspect that the moon has a cool, solid core and, therefore, accumulated from cold debris or was torn from the earth. If a body the size of the moon was formed in either of these two ways, it should not be hot enough to have a molten core. In a body the size of the earth, on the other hand, the core is subjected to such pressure and heating by radioactive elements in its interior that it must turn fluid.

The theory that the moon was formed by accretion of debris is supported, some investigators think, by the fact that it has a slightly elongated shape—that is, it bulges in the direction of the earth by about three-fifths of a mile, with a corresponding bulge believed to exist on the other side. Calculations show that the moon could not support such a bulge if it had a liquid or nearly liquid interior; therefore, according to the theory, it must be solid all the way through.

One explanation of the lunar bulge is that it was formed by a few very large meteoroids among those that went into the making of the moon. Another is that the earth's gravitational attraction pulled the moon out of shape long ago before the two had solidified. This latter explanation fits the theory that the earth and moon both were molten at one time and that they used to be much closer than they are today. The lunar bulge is bigger than the earth's pull would produce at the moon's present distance from us.

The idea that the earth and moon were once much closer is supported by comparison of modern and Babylonian and Egyptian records of eclipses. The ancients recorded eclipses at times when, according to modern calculations, they should not have occurred. The explanation for this is that the earth's rate of rotation is slowing down; the globe spins slower today than it did in ancient times. The slowdown, at the rate of about one-thousandth of a second per century, is the result of the tides, or bulges, the moon's pull raises in the earth's oceans and crust. The bulges act like giant brake shoes, dragging against the earth as it spins beneath them. A result of the slowdown is that the moon is moving farther from the earth at the rate of about an inch a year. The spinning of the earth tends to drag the tidal bulges in the direction of its spin, and the bulges pull on the moon a little bit, too. The result is that the moon is being accelerated by a slight amount in its orbit and, therefore, spirals outward from the earth.

One of the most puzzling aspects of the moon is its low density. The earth's average density is 5.5 times that of water, while the density of the moon, as calculated from astronomical observations, is 3.3. If the earth and moon formed near each other as separate condensations, why should one be denser than the other? Or if they are the result of accretion of smaller chunks of matter, why should one collect denser objects than the other?

The difference in density would seem to fit very nicely with the old idea that the moon was torn from the earth, for its density is about the same as that of rock lying near the earth's surface. The trouble with this theory is the size of the moon in relation to the earth. The theory would be acceptable, perhaps, for other planets whose moons are much smaller than their parents. But to have a moon so large whirled out of the earth seems unacceptable to most scientists.

Other lunar mysteries, which scientists hope can be solved readily by manned exploration, include the origin of the craters and maria. The moon's surface is pocked with thousands of craters ranging from less than a mile in diameter to nearly 200 miles across. (Plate 12.) Some craters have walls rising as high as 20,000 feet from floors that are generally lower than the surrounding terrain. Frequently there are mountain peaks rising from the centers of craters. Large portions of the moon are literally riddled with craters, giving the moon the appearance of having gone through a cosmic bombardment. (Plate 13.) But is this the result of bombardment or did volcanoes produce the craters? And what accounts for the large, smooth maria—are they lava flows or bowls of dust? Some craters have been partially covered by whatever produced the maria, appearing as ghost outlines on the lunar seas. (Plate 12.)

There are two main theories concerning crater formation. One is that they were caused by meteoroid impacts. In several hundred years of observation, astronomers have been unable to tell whether any new craters have been formed in this way. However, there probably are fewer meteoroids in the solar system now than in earlier times, particularly the larger ones, so the fact that we have identified no newly created marks isn't much of a clue. The other explanation of the craters is that they were caused by volcanoes.

Both theories could be correct as far as we can tell by observation from earth. Some craters obviously were formed by objects striking the moon with great force, splattering material in ray patterns which resemble the result of bomb explosions. And many of them overlap, which doesn't seem a likely result of volcanic action. At the same time, there are small craters on mountain tops, too many to have been put there by random fall of meteoroids. Many smaller craters also are distributed in linear patterns, another feature which makes meteoric origin seem improbable for them.

Lunar explorers will search craters for volcanic materials. One crater in particular, Alphonsus (Plate 12.), deserves such investigation since astronomers in recent years have reported seeing what appear to be occasional eruptions of gas from smaller craters inside it and a mountain peak in its center.

As for the maria, the theory favored most is that they were formed when huge bodies struck the moon, the impacts generating enough heat to melt large quantities of rock. If lava was produced on the moon, a great deal of water vapor should have been released from the melted rock.

While the lunar expedition currently is the primary goal of the U.S. space program, it is by no means the most important objective from the scientific point of view, nor is exploration of the planets. Just as important is investigation of space itself and the various phenomena encountered there. This is the aim of such NASA programs as the aforementioned Orbiting Solar Observatory (OSO), and Orbiting Geophysical Observatory (OGO), as well as other satellite programs and numerous atmospheric and space probes. Homer E. Newell, director of NASA's Office of Space Sciences, stressed this aspect of space exploration in testimony before the House Science and Astronautics Committee:

> One might well ask ... if there is so little matter in interplanetary space, why should there be a great interest in it? The first answer, perhaps, is that the question as phrased implies a misconception. Actually, there is more than just a little matter in space. Indeed, the total amount of matter in the space between the stars of our galaxy adds up to at least the amount contained in the stars. It is just that the space throughout which this matter is dispersed is so vast that the matter exists at a very low density. So we are not talking about a small amount of matter, but rather a lot of matter under conditions of low density. Indeed, this interplanetary material, existing at such very low densities, and embedded in the weak magnetic fields that pervade the regions of the solar system, exists under conditions that are unattainable in the laboratory. We have, therefore, an opportunity to study matter and physical processes under conditions that reveal much about the fundamental nature of the universe.[*]

[*] From a statement before Subcommittee No. 3, Committee on Science and Astronautics, House of Representatives, 1962.

Although the stars and galaxies are still very much beyond the puny reach of man and his rockets, space technology also is enabling a vast improvement in investigations beyond the solar system. On earth, telescopes have practically reached the limit of their "seeing" ability with the 200-inch instrument at Mount Palomar because of atmospheric interference. The atmosphere filters out most of the radiation emitted by stars, leaving only the small visible light portion for study by optical instruments. Once placed above the atmosphere, a much smaller telescope can examine galaxies several times farther away than the most distant our biggest earth-bound telescopes can see. That is the aim of NASA's Orbiting Astronomical Observatory (OAO), a 3,500-pound satellite carrying a thirty-six-inch telescope.

IX. THE MILITARY
IN SPACE

THERE is still considerable question, even in the military mind, that a military mission exists in space beyond improvements in reconnaissance, communications, navigation, and weather forecasting. The spacecraft in its present stage of development is in the same military position as the aircraft was years ago when airplanes were useful mainly for intelligence-gathering activities.

Whether the spacecraft will follow the pattern of aircraft development and progress to bombing and combat missions is the big question the military seeks to answer. And that question is a matter not only of technical feasibility but military desirability. It may be technically possible to build a spacecraft to do this or that job in space, but it also may be a waste of effort and money, and perhaps be disastrous as well.

A proposal to put large bombs in orbit illustrates the point. There is nothing technically impossible about putting bombs in orbit and then bringing them down to destroy targets on earth. For that matter, nuclear bombs of sufficient size wouldn't have to be brought back; they would be effective if detonated a couple of hundred miles over a target. But is there any point in going to the trouble and expense of developing such weapons when we already have ocean-spanning missiles that, while they may take a few minutes longer to reach target, can destroy just as effectively?

It has been argued that ICBMs can be spotted in time for a threatened nation to launch its retaliatory missiles, whereas a satellite bomb would be an effective sneak weapon, regarded as just another research satellite by the intended victim until the aggressor was ready to push the button. However, in today's state of the art in nuclear warfare, an aggressor must wipe out most of the victim's retaliatory capability on the first strike or face destruction himself. Such a strike against the United States would require a force of satellites exploded at nearly the same instant over known and hidden targets dispersed around the world, an impossible task. Moreover, it is doubtful that either the United States or Russia is going to let the other build up such a patterned force of satellites in orbit. This country already is carefully tracking and monitoring all known satellites and is working to improve its ability to spot any that may be sneaked into orbit. We assume that Russia is developing and maintaining a similar space watch.

Gen. Bernard A. Schriever, chief of the Air Force Systems Command, which would provide such weapons if they were called for, testified before the House Science and Astronautics subcommittee that the value of large bombs in orbit is questionable when viewed in the light of their worth as "stabilizing or retaliatory factors."

Also questionable is the feasibility of manned military spacecraft. Although man has been launched into orbit and returned safely a number of times, we still do not know how well he can function in space, how he would be affected by

130

prolonged weightlessness and radiation. The *Apollo* trip will provide some of the answers.

While facing this state of affairs with regard to military applications of spacecraft, we also face certain Space Age military problems. As outlined before the House Committee on Armed Services by Lt. Gen. James Ferguson, deputy Air Force chief of staff for research and technology, they are:

• A marked imbalance exists between the Soviet bloc and the Free World relating to intelligence activities.

• U.S. defense against Soviet ICBMs is inadequate in event deterrence fails.

• The Soviets have demonstrated increasing competency in space technology which—who knows at this point—could lead to a number of space weapons.

The Air Force, as the service responsible for most of the research, development, test, and evaluation of Defense Department space projects, believes *potential* solutions to these problems are offered by space technology. It stresses "potential" because much basic and applied research, including development of experimental spacecraft, remains to be done to determine both feasibility and desirability.

These possible solutions are stated in a highly classified document, the Air Force Space Plan, which summarizes long-range needs and identifies "technological objectives." To meet these objectives, all U.S. defense agencies are devoting study and other effort to a number of technical areas, some of which are not common to the civilian-scientific program. As can be seen, some of the objectives involve rather futuristic ideas, but as one technologist has put it: "It is essential that we assess the probable future of space flight with full realization that excessive conservatism and technological caution may be even more dangerous than over-optimism; that technology will grow at least as fast in the

131

future as in the past, and that new scientific and engineering breakthroughs are inevitable." *

The areas include:

Manned Spacecraft—Characteristics of manned military spacecraft will be considerably different from manned vehicles designed for scientific research. These differences are related to such things as launch response time, maneuverability in orbit, maneuverability during reentry into the atmosphere, precision landing, vehicle reuse after minimum refurbishing, and incorporation of weapons.

Rendezvous—The military wants to be able to rendezvous with, inspect, and destroy unidentified satellites and spacecraft. Rendezvous between friendly spacecraft, as in the scientific program, poses a much simpler problem than trying to intercept a hostile vehicle.

Maneuverability—Both manned and unmanned military craft will require a degree of maneuverability not essential to scientific operations. This will involve special design of in-space propulsion systems.

Reentry and Recovery—Much basic work remains to be done on techniques for returning manned and unmanned craft from space. Ballistic reentry, in which a vehicle such as the *Mercury* capsule simply falls back, popping a parachute after reaching the denser atmosphere, does not make good sense for the military, which desires a winged, maneuverable ship that can take off, fly into space, and then return to land like a conventional aircraft. Such returns are made with the X-15, but true spacecraft travel four or five times faster, posing greater problems in combating reentry heating.

Launch Vehicles—If routine and quick-reaction military operations are to become practical, booster rockets must be

* Dandridge M. Cole, General Electric consulting astronautical engineer.

made more reliable and their cost brought down. The current cost of launching spacecraft is too high for extensive military use. Development of solid-fuel and nuclear rockets and ways to recover boosters will reduce costs.

Space Environmental Data—Need for this is common to both scientific and military programs. However, the military requirement for quick action at any time makes especially critical the need for accurate prediction of space "weather" —solar flares.

Bioastronautics Equipment—NASA's manned projects will provide much data here, but the Air Force feels it needs an orbiting military space laboratory for extensive test of men and specialized equipment.

Weapons Effect—The effect of weapons on vehicles in space must be investigated to determine possibilities of offense and defense.

Communications—The best possible communications are imperative for command and control of existing and future military forces. We need reliable, worldwide, jam-resistant radio communications. The Project West Ford concept, mentioned earlier, looks promising.*

Sensing Devices—Development of better infrared sensors, cameras, and radars will enable further improvements in reconnaissance and early warning.

There are many specific projects in these and other areas to determine feasibility of proposals or to develop those which appear attainable. Some of the projects are well under way, and a few have been successfully completed or nearly so. At this time some are worth only study effort. Others, the military complains, are worth more effort but have not been pushed fast enough because of high-level decisions to keep them in the study stage or restrict them to relatively small research efforts, similar to the X-15 proj-

* See Chapter VII.

ect, rather than allow them full-scale military development status.

By agency, the programs * include:

ADVANCED RESEARCH PROJECTS AGENCY

BAMBI—A research effort aimed at development of a ballistic-missile interception system using satellite-based spacecraft to intercept and destroy enemy missiles during the boost phase of flight. Considerably more than ten satellites would be needed. This is part of Project Defender, a program in which all services are studying defense against missiles and spacecraft.

ARENTS—ARPA Environmental Test Satellite to investigate space conditions in 22,000-mile-high orbits where it would be advantageous to place communications and other satellites. Contracts have been awarded for three satellites to determine the space environment's long-term effect on materials, lubricants, bearings, etc.

VELA HOTEL—A research and development project aimed at devising a six-satellite system for detecting nuclear explosions in space.

PRESS—Pacific Range Electromagnetic Signature Study for an advanced radar system to detect approaching ICBM warheads. Part of Defender. "Signature" refers to the disturbance or trail an object makes in passing through the atmosphere or the tenuous gas of space. Radar can detect the trail of ionized gas left in the air by a meteor. Objects of different shape and size might produce characteristic signatures, in which case radar could distinguish a warhead from a meteor or decoy object.

RBS—Random Barrage System. Study of the feasibility of placing 20,000 to 100,000 armed satellites into random orbits as a defensive measure against enemy ICBMs.

* The names became informal after Department of Defense ordered use of secret numbers instead.

AIR FORCE

AEROSPACE PLANE (ASP)—Research program to develop a manned spacecraft able to take off and land like an aircraft. Separate studies are under way by six defense contractors.

DISCOVERER—The most successful military satellite program to date. Designed to probe space conditions, develop means of recovering satellite payloads, and provide a test-bed for satellite research programs such as *Midas* and *Samos,* it has resulted in return of numerous capsules from orbit.

X-20 (DYNA-SOAR)—Research and development effort to produce a manned orbital "boost-glide" spacecraft with wings. A primary aim is to develop controlled reentry as opposed to the Project Mercury ballistic-type return. A follow-on to the X-15 project, it will also investigate the feasibility of a spacecraft for orbital reconnaissance and defense and offense. It will be launched into space by a *Titan III* booster. There are complaints about this being held to an X-15 type research program.

ORION—Engineering study for a space booster launched by a series of atomic explosions.

SAINT—Satellite Inspector. Research and development program for a spacecraft to inspect unidentified satellites. Contracts for development and testing have been let. *Saint I,* an unmanned craft using TV-camera eyes will be placed in orbit ahead of the target and use retro-rockets for rendezvous. Also under study are manned satellite inspection spacecraft.

MIDAS—Missile Defense Alarm System consisting of early-warning satellites equipped with infrared sensors to detect enemy ICBM launches. The system may use up to fifteen satellites in polar orbit.

SAMOS—Surveillance and Missile Observation Satellite. Also nearing operational status, this polar-orbiting satellite is equipped with high-resolution cameras. Pictures can be received by both radio and capsule return.

MILITARY TEST SPACE STATION—In the study stage so far, this would provide a twelve-man space station for research into all aspects of the military possibilities in space, including rendezvous and interception techniques. Spacecraft to ferry the crew to and from the station could grow out of other study and research programs.

SLOMAR—Space Logistics, Maintenance and Rescue craft. Feasibility studies by defense contractors have been under way for some time. Such a vehicle would be needed to support military space operations.

GLOBAL SURVEILLANCE SYSTEM—Study for a manned reconnaissance-strike spacecraft.

ORBITAL WEAPONS SYSTEM—Studies of orbital bombing systems.

As a launcher for many of its vehicles well into the 1970's, the Air Force will use a big *Titan III* "space truck" booster able to place 12½ tons into a 300-mile orbit. The booster consists of a liquid-fueled *Titan II* ICBM with two 120-inch diameter solid rockets strapped to its sides. The solid rockets are built in segments that can be put together in varying numbers according to the thrust desired. With a maximum of five segments bolted together each solid rocket will produce more than 1,000,000 pounds of thrust, giving *Titan III* a total first-stage thrust of more than 2,000,000 pounds. The strap-on rockets are more than twice the fifty-six-inch diameter of the *Minuteman* ICBM.

ARMY

SECOR—Sequential Collation of Range. A Corps of Engineers project to produce a satellite device for geodetic measurements of high accuracy.

NIKE-ZEUS—A 200-mile range antimissile missile designed to destroy ICBM warheads in the terminal phase of flight.

LAMP—Lunar Analysis and Mapping Program. Corps of Engineers is producing a lunar topographical map and expects to achieve high accuracy by using photographs obtained by lunar probes in the scientific space program.

NAVY

TRANSIT—A navigational system which, using four transmitting satellites, enables *Polaris* submarines and other craft to fix their positions with great accuracy regardless of weather.

YO-YO—Study for a photoreconnaissance satellite to be launched at sea, make one orbit, and be recovered.

The Navy also has looked at the possibilities of launching small satellites from carrier-based fighter aircraft and launching satellites from ships with the *Polaris* missile.

A joint project involving all of the services and NASA is a geodetic satellite called *Anna,* now in research and development, for intercontinental surveying.

Another joint effort involving all services is the Department of Defense communications satellite program. One project in this program is aimed at demonstrating the feasibility of a 1,250-pound repeater satellite operating in a 22,000-mile orbit. Three such satellites placed at intervals of 120 degrees around the earth would provide continuous communications coverage around the globe. Also planned is a system of medium-altitude communications satellites. The Air Force is responsible for development, production, and launch of space devices necessary to establish these systems, while the Army will develop the required ground communication systems, and the Navy will provide one or more shipborne communication stations.

Of immediate and increasing importance to the military is the need for continuous surveillance of space. With such installations as the Air Force-operated Space Detection and

Tracking System (SPADATS) and the Navy-operated Space Surveillance Facility (SPASUR), the United States is able to maintain a log from which can be determined at any given moment the present, past, or future paths of known satellites. These systems are tied to the Ballistic Missile Early Warning System (BMEWS), which uses radar to detect missiles in flight. SPASUR is able to detect and determine the orbits of space objects over the United States at altitudes of up to 1,000 miles.

Work is in progress to stretch the surveillance network's reach to the moon. The program includes an intensive examination of space between the earth and the moon for any other natural satellites astronomers may have missed. The idea is to establish a complete inventory of everything in orbit in earth-moon space so the surveillance system can tell when something is added.

Looking to the future, the Air Force has been conducting studies into the possible strategic worth of the moon and interplanetary space. One suggestion is that the moon could be used for deployment of deterrent weapons.

At the same time the Army has drawn up plans for a research facility to simulate the moon environment so engineers can develop the construction techniques and equipment that would be required to build a military lunar base.

Are such ideas pure science fiction? Military men admit they don't know at this time. But they point to a thought-provoking theory concerning the possible long-range value of space which effectively sums up the military attitude. Known as the Panama Theory or Panama Canal concept, it states:

"There are dominant areas of space which, though distant, may be of vital strategic importance to future national survival."

X. CONQUEST OF THE SOLAR SYSTEM

THE planets most likely to harbor other life in the solar system lie within a broad temperate zone around the sun. This "life belt," stretching 75,000,000 miles from Venus to the orbit of Mars, represents the zone, or *ecosphere,* around the sun in which the ranges of heat, light, water, and oxygen could be suitable for life as we know it. Venus orbits on the hot border of the belt, the earth plies the moderate middle, and Mars swings around the cold outer boundary.

There is good reason for thinking that only in this zone is life possible. The sun's innermost planet, Mercury, hot enough to melt lead on its surface, is too hot for life based on any conceivable chemistry. The complicated chemical structures necessary for matter to assume the delicately balanced living state simply cannot hold together in such heat. At the other extreme, although it is disputable, the outer planets could be so cold that the chemical activity implicit in any definition of life is unable to occur.

Thus, it may be that Venus and Mars alone hold promise of life, although some experts do not exclude other planets or even the moon. However, their presence in the solar temperate zone is no guarantee that they will have it, as indicated by the first space-probe examination of Venus.

Several billion years ago all of the planets, according to a widely held theory, may have had atmospheres of about the same gaseous mixture, but eons of solar radiation have changed them. As we have seen, the hot, small planets would lose gases and water vapor. Venus, being only a little smaller than the earth, might be expected to have retained the same kind of atmosphere but for the fact that it receives nearly twice as much solar radiation.

We have been able to detect little, if any, water vapor in the Venusian atmosphere, and no free oxygen. There is some uncertainty about these results, however. It could be that any water in the planet's atmosphere is in the form of liquid or ice which the instruments used cannot detect. But a high concentration of carbon dioxide has been detected, 500 times as much as on earth, which has only three parts in 10,000 parts of air.

Before investigation of Venus by an American space probe in late 1962, the high carbon dioxide content had led to two diametrically opposed theories about Venus, splitting the experts into two camps, the "drys" and the "wets." One camp held that the carbon dioxide meant Venus was a vast desert. The other contended that it meant just the opposite, that Venus was almost completely covered with ocean.

How could two such different ideas have come from the same evidence?

Both were based on this fact: In the presence of water, carbon dioxide reacts with silicates—sand—to form rock.

So, said the drys, if there was an abundance of water on Venus, most of the carbon dioxide would have been used up by now, taken out of the atmosphere to make rock. But since there is so much of this gas in the planet's atmosphere, it must be that Venus has little, if any, water.

But, said the wets, if Venus was nearly covered with ocean,

140

the carbon dioxide would react in the water to form a solid layer of rock on the ocean floors. Once this layer was formed —and it would take only a thin one, the argument went— the gas could reach no more silicate to form rock and, thus, would have to stay in the atmosphere.

Most experts took the dry view, leading to a widespread belief that Venus could have no life. This view was supported by the first robot explorer to examine Venus, a *Mariner* spacecraft that flew by the planet at a distance of some 21,000 miles on December 14, 1962. Scanning Venus with special instruments as it flew past, *Mariner* reported the planet has a surface temperature of about 800 degrees F., more than enough to melt lead, and too hot for any life as we know it. According to some theorists, however, this doesn't rule out the possibility that microorganisms could exist in the cool, upper layers of Venus' atmosphere.

Until the *Mariner* flight, science knew much less about Venus than Mars, even though Mars is, on the average, nearly twice as far from us. Telescopes never have been able to see through Venus' opaque atmosphere to its surface. (Plate 14.)

On the other hand, we have been able to see and roughly map Mars's surface through its thin, transparent atmosphere. (Plate 15.) We know that its period of rotation is only a few minutes longer than earth's, that it has seasonal formation of polar caps which come and go like a light frost, and that there are dark greenish areas—maria—which vary in location, size, and shape with the seasons, suggesting vegetation. While there is some controversy over what causes the dark areas, there is general agreement they are not oceans and that Mars is mostly desert.

The planet's surface temperature is estimated to range from −60 degrees F. at night to 75 degrees during the day in the deserts and 90 degrees in the dark areas. Spectrographic studies show its atmosphere may be mostly nitrogen, containing practically no oxygen. But two substances necessary for plant life as we know it—water vapor and carbon dioxide (much less than on Venus)—are there, meaning that, chemically, plant life is possible.

Considering all of these things, most scientists believe Mars probably has plant life. This belief is strengthened by the fact that the maria reappear following what seem to be frequent dust storms on the planet. Growing plants could account for this. Laboratory experiments which show that some types of bacteria not only survive but flourish under simulated Martian conditions also lend support to the idea that life can exist on Mars.

However, the fact that little, if any, oxygen has been detected may mean that higher life forms are unlikely on Mars. Some low forms such as anaerobic bacteria do not require oxygen, but all advanced earth life must have it in order to obtain energy.*

In the past some scientific authorities have speculated, even insisted, that the network of long, dark lines on Mars was a planet-wide system of canals created by intelligent beings. It was noted that the canals emanated from dark, circular spots which were labeled "oases." This idea now is regarded as a completely unfounded theory brought about in part because the markings originally were called *canali* by Italian astronomer Giovanni Schiaparelli, who discovered them in 1877. *Canali,* meaning "channels," was translated to "canals," and imagination ran rampant.

A more recent idea is that the lines are fractures caused by asteroid impacts. Another is that they are ray systems of debris formed when objects splattered on Mars's surface. This latter theory notes that the ray systems are similar to those on the moon, with a significant difference—the moon's ray systems are light in color, whereas those on Mars are dark. Why the difference? One idea says that Mars has

* See Chapter XI.

142

vegetation which seeks the warmth and protection of the broken rock debris in the rays and dark spots. This theory adds: "Give the moon an atmosphere and some plants, and its rays would turn dark."

All things considered, Mars is the first choice for manned expeditions. Mars's climate is somewhat like that of a high-altitude desert, and it has been suggested that in some of its lower valleys, explorers, previously conditioned in high-altitude chambers, could dispense with space suits and walk around with only breathing equipment.

The first direct exploration of the planets involves so-called fly-by and orbiter missions throughout the middle and late 1960's by robot vehicles. The planetary atmospheric and surface conditions must be reconnoitered in missions of this type before satisfactory spacecraft can be designed to descend and land for surface investigation. Engineers think techniques and designs developed for earth atmospheric re-entry probably can be used for Mars entry since that planet has a relatively thin atmosphere. Venus appears to have a much denser atmosphere, and poses a more difficult entry problem. Also, Venus landings might be quite hazardous since we cannot see, at least from the earth, what the surface is like. Perhaps this cannot be determined until instruments actually are landed.

The NASA vehicle designed for Venus and Mars fly-by missions is the *Mariner*, a 600- to 1,200-pound spacecraft equipped with instruments for photo and radar reconnaissance of the planetary surfaces, determination of atmospheric and surface temperatures, identification of atmospheric makeup, measurement of magnetic fields and possible radiation belts, and exploration of the interplanetary fields and particles between earth and her neighbors.

With modifications, the spacecraft is suitable for investigation of both Venus and Mars. One modification involves its solar panels which protrude winglike from its stubby body and convert solar radiation into power to operate equipment. In the vicinity of Mars, about two and a half times more solar panel area is required than at Venus to collect enough power. Another difference in equipment is the need for radar, rather than cameras, to penetrate Venus opaque atmosphere.

An advanced *Mariner* version will be able to carry a small capsule to be ejected into the planetary atmospheres for direct measurements on the surface while the parent spacecraft continues observations as it passes.

Voyager, a 2,400-pound explorer, extends *Mariner's* capability considerably. One version is designed to enter an orbit about the target planet and inject a 700-pound TV and instrument capsule for ground observation. Some 60 to 85 per cent of *Voyager's* weight is devoted to retro-propulsion and terminal guidance equipment needed to put it into orbit at destination. The orbiting spacecraft observes the planet and its atmosphere from an altitude of several hundred miles while the landing payload makes detailed measurements during parachute descent and on the ground.

The most important ground observations include identification of any life and discovery of what could be harmful to future manned expeditions.

Instruments that can be used for detecting life include high-resolution TV cameras that would spot larger living forms if the capsule lands in an area where they are abundant. However, science believes the chances are greater for finding microscopic organisms—such as bacteria—since they are so prolific on earth and are more likely to be found wherever instruments are landed on a planet. One instrument planned for this is a TV-microscope arrangement enabling scientists to view directly any organisms found.

Another method for life-detection involves use of a sticky string about 100 feet long and contained in a device about the size of a pint jar. The string is shot out with a projectile and then wound back into a nutrient broth in which metabolic carbon dioxide is detected if organisms grow and multiply. NASA reported an earth field test of this device registered a positive signal within forty-five minutes.

Fly-by missions to the immediately more distant planets, Mercury and Jupiter, are expected by perhaps 1970. Early Mercury missions will concentrate on photographing that planet's surface, one side of which is believed to face the sun at all times. Mercury is thought to be very much like the moon in appearance, and chances for life seem nil.

While it is generally believed that Jupiter (Plate 15.) and the other large outer planets are too cold for life, there are experts who dispute this. One is Dr. Carl Sagan, of the Space Sciences Laboratory and Department of Astronomy at the University of California, who thinks the chances for life on Jupiter may be good. Since astronomers have measured temperatures of 220 degrees below zero Fahrenheit and colder in Jupiter's ammonia and methane clouds, it has been regarded as likely that the planet's surface is also extremely cold. But Sagan presents a picture in which light penetrates Jupiter's clouds to the surface, the surface absorbs it and then emits infrared radiation which cannot escape into space. This would produce a "greenhouse" effect in which the temperature rises on the planet's surface, possible to 70 degrees or more. The earth presents a similar picture, with temperatures of -150 degrees F. measured fifty miles above its warm surface. The "greenhouse" effect is to be expected on any planet with an atmosphere.

Further, Sagan points to results of simulated atmospheric studies which show that simple organic molecules must be produced in the Jovian atmosphere by the action of ultraviolet light from the sun and atmospheric electrical discharges. The planet's atmosphere contains hydrogen, ammonia, and methane. According to current theory, this kind of atmosphere, although poisonous to life as we know it, may very well have been the kind from which the primordial constituents of life were produced on earth.

The theory proposes that the primitive earth had this sort of atmosphere and water vapor, but no oxygen since the latter attacks and destroys organic compounds. It is held that had the earth's oxygen not been chemically bound in other substances such as water and metal oxides during the early days, it would have prevented accumulation of organic matter. It was following creation of life, which through constant production of energy and growth resists chemical attack, that free oxygen appeared in quantity on earth—the product of living things themselves.

Sagan, after producing organic compounds in his experiments with a simulated Jovian atmosphere, estimated that organic molecules might be created at the rate of more than ten pounds per square mile per year on Jupiter. It has been suggested that life on Jupiter would have to adapt to tremendous pressure, like deep-sea life, since the planet's atmosphere may be thousands of miles thick, compressing to liquid at great depths.

Since scientists believe Jupiter's atmosphere, perhaps more than the nearer planets, resembles earth's primordial atmosphere, the first instrument probes to Jupiter will carry out a spectrophotometric experiment to see if simple organic molecules have been formed.

There is an interesting sidelight in this speculation about creation of life on other planets. In experiments in which protein-like particles have been formed in the laboratory, the amount of gravity acting during the process helps determine the size of the particle formed—according to a NASA report: "Large if formed on Jupiter and small if formed on Mars."

Natural radio signals emitted from Jupiter pose some interesting mysteries. There are two distinct kinds of signals, one continuous and weak, the other sporadic and quite

146

strong. The steady signals are produced in the atmosphere. Any excited gas gives off radio waves. The other signals, coming in short bursts, last only up to a second and occur only when a certain side of Jupiter is facing earth, meaning that the sources are at some fixed location. Many bursts have been recorded on each ten-hour revolution of the planet.

There has been speculation that the sporadic radio noises are caused by huge volcanic eruptions which set up oscillations in the Jovian atmosphere, or by tremendous lightning flashes. More recent suggestions are that the various noise sources could be the result of interactions between the atmosphere and intense radiation belts such as surround the earth. Some signals apparently come from Jupiter's giant oval-shaped red spot which is believed to be an atmospheric phenomenon, perhaps an accumulation of clouds over some ground feature. The spot, which has its own rotation period around the planet as do other markings, was about 30,000 miles long and 7,000 miles wide when discovered in the nineteenth century. It is somewhat smaller now.

All of the large outer planets, Jupiter, Saturn, Uranus, and Neptune, are huge compared to the inner planets, ranging in diameter from 88,000 miles for Jupiter to 31,000 miles for Neptune. Their composition and structure is generally supposed to be the same, one theory being that they have rock or metallic cores surrounded by layers of ice thousands of miles deep and atmospheres 2,000 to 8,000 miles thick.

Pluto (Plate 15.) is in its own way the most mysterious of the outer planets because there is so much doubt about its size. Its diameter has been measured as about half that of earth, but that doesn't fit calculations that have to do with disturbances caused in the motion of Neptune and Uranus. These disturbances led to predictions of Pluto's existence long before it was found. But the predictions called for a much more massive planet than Pluto, which seems too small to have much gravitational effect on giants such as Neptune and

Uranus. There has been speculation that perhaps the Mount Palomar telescope measured not the true diameter of Pluto but that of a huge bright spot of reflection. We might see sunlight reflected from Pluto in this manner if the planet was covered with a frozen methane ocean and was, therefore, a very smooth and shiny sphere.

Plans for the more advanced instrument missions to Jupiter and points beyond, including orbiting and landing, remain indefinite since the heavier payloads and longer distances will require use of nuclear electric propulsion, currently under development.

As for manned trips to the big planets, there are many more difficulties involved than for the nearer bodies, not the least of which is the strength of the giants' gravitational fields. Jupiter's velocity of escape is five times the earth's, Saturn's is more than three times as great, and escape from the other large planets would require twice as much speed as we need to leave the earth.

Nuclear rockets definitely are required. However, even then it is difficult to envision manned landings on the big planets. Instrument landings will be tough enough on Jupiter where even metals could flow under the tremendous pressures of an atmosphere that may be 8,000 miles deep.

For these reasons some experts propose that manned expeditions land on the moons of the outer planets, establishing bases from which they can send down probes and conduct experiments. These men regard it as no great stretch of the imagination to think that some day, perhaps well before the end of the century, there will be manned expeditions on the moons of Jupiter, Saturn, Uranus, and Neptune. There are plenty of moons available for such expeditions since the big four planets have a total of twenty-eight. Some of these moons, it is believed, could provide refueling for spaceships since they appear to have an abundance of methane gas.

Jupiter offers the widest selection of moons with a dozen

satellites, 14 to 3,200 miles across, scattered 113,000 to 15,000,000 miles from the planet. Saturn's nine moons run 150 to 3,500 miles in diameter and are located 185,000 to 13,000,000 miles from their parent. Uranus has five satellites, largest of which is 1,000 miles across. The solar system's smallest known moons belong to Mars, which has Phobos, seven miles in diameter, and Deimos, five miles across.

Space enthusiasts also think the asteroid belt, lying between Mars and Jupiter and composed of thousands of barren chunks of rock, might provide some refueling stations for space voyagers. Two of the larger asteroids are Ceres and Pallas, 500 and 304 miles in diameter.

Going beyond mere passive use of the other bodies in the solar system, some scientists propose that in time man will be able to rearrange the solar system to please himself, changing the orbits of planets and otherwise making them more suitable for his purposes.

XI. SPAWN OF THE STARS

THE more man has learned about the earth and the surrounding universe, the more his ego has suffered, for one by one science has demolished ideas that the earth and its life are unique.

Science today, operating on the logic that the laws and consequences of nature are the same throughout the universe, regards planets and life as legitimate manifestations of the evolution of matter, not as cosmic accidents. It is as convinced of the existence of other life-bearing planets around other stars as it is that the earth is round. The only thing that remains speculative about the subject is just how the evolution of matter proceeds, resulting in creation of stars, planets and, eventually, intelligent life in the universe.

Although science cannot say how the material of the universe came into being, it has discerned that all matter consists of just three fundamental building blocks. These basic units are the electron, the proton (nucleus of the hydrogen atom), and the neutron. Using just these particles, nature builds the atoms of all the elements, from hydrogen to uranium.

As the simplest element, hydrogen is the most abundant material in the universe, accounting for more than 75 per cent of the weight of all matter in space. Great clouds of hydrogen gas, mixed with dust, are concentrated in the spiral arms of our galaxy and in the arms of other galaxies of the same type. Fields of stars often are embedded in such clouds. Some clouds are luminous and can be seen with optical telescopes. Others are dark and opaque, their presence being known because they block light from stars lying beyond. Since the interstellar hydrogen atoms emit energy in the form of radio noise, the distribution of the gas-dust clouds in space also can be traced with radio telescopes. Using both visual and radio means to detect the clouds, astronomers have mapped the spiral arms of the galaxy.

Accompanying the basic building blocks and governing the interactions of all matter in the universe are just three fundamental physical forces—the nuclear force, the electromagnetic force, and gravity.

The nuclear force is the most powerful, binding protons and neutrons together to form the nucleus of the atom. This force of attraction is so great that the nucleus is almost unbelievably compact, having a density of a billion tons per cubic inch.

Second strongest is the electromagnetic force, which completes the atom by binding electrons to the nucleus. Some 100 times weaker than the nuclear force, it also binds atoms into molecules.

Weakest force is gravity. Its strength is infinitesimal compared to the nuclear force, yet it is sufficient to bind together larger collections of matter, such as the solar system and the galaxy.

The least powerful force plays the major role in the early stages of the evolution of matter. Stars are believed to begin as centers of turbulence in gas-dust clouds. Astronomers have photographed clouds containing numbers of small, dark globules which may be condensations on their way to becoming stars. When such centers form, the particles in them are drawn closer by gravity and squeezed into an ever-smaller volume over millions of years. Under the resulting pressure, the temperature of the central core rises to something like 15 million degrees, and nuclear reactions among the particles in the mass are ignited spontaneously.

At this point, the binding energy of the nuclear force comes into play. The process essentially is one in which the particles collide with each other at high speed, four hydrogen nuclei combining to form a nucleus of helium, the second most abundant element in the universe. In these collisions, a small amount of the particles' mass is converted to a relatively large amount of energy, thus producing not only helium, the next highest element on the evolutionary scale, but releasing energy as well.*

The combining of hydrogen nuclei to form helium is known as thermonuclear fusion, the same thing that occurs in the explosion of hydrogen bombs. The hot cores of stars are ideal for this process, which requires high speed and frequent collisions among the nuclei. The higher the temperature, the greater the commotion among the particles inside stars. The resulting high internal pressure counteracts gravitational contraction so that a star reaches a state of equilibrium between the nuclear and gravitational forces.

Of this much in the evolution of matter science is certain, for it has duplicated the phenomenon in the hydrogen bomb. Beyond this point, however, there are two main theories as to how all of the elements were produced.

One theory continues along the route just described, seeing the conversion of hydrogen to helium as the first step in a "cooking" process in which all elements are built up from hydrogen. The theory draws this picture:

With hydrogen being used to create helium, the amount

* Einstein predicted this in his famous equation, $E=mc^2$.

of helium in a star gradually increases at the expense of the former. Since helium doesn't "burn" at the same temperature as hydrogen, the hydrogen-burning must eventually be slowed, at which stage the core cools and the star begins to contract again under the force of gravity. This leads to further compression in the star, raising the temperature to a level where helium itself starts to burn. When this occurs, contraction is stopped while the next step in the evolution of matter takes place.

In this stage, three helium nuclei are combined to form one heavier carbon nucleus, with additional release of enormous energy. As in the first stage, the helium is consumed until the central fire is dampened again, the core cools, the star contracts, the temperature rises again, and the third step in the cooking procedure gets under way.

In this manner successively heavier elements are built up until the iron group of elements is reached. At this point, about halfway between the lightest and heaviest elements, the buildup stops, for iron, most stable of the elements, absorbs energy instead of releasing it and ends the burning process.

Again the core of the star cools. As in the earlier stages, gravitational attraction once more gains the upper hand, but this time with catastrophic results—the star actually collapses in a matter of seconds, and the high temperatures and pressures bring the star's end. It explodes.

In order to produce the heavy elements beyond iron, a "second generation" star is necessary. When the first type of star explodes, it spews all of its matter, including the heavier elements it has manufactured, in all directions. These mix with the gas-dust clouds in interstellar space and, over the eons, new stars condense from the enriched material. The newcomers, having a mixture of heavier elements from the beginning, go on to produce the rest. Scientists believe they have convincing evidence that stars produce heavier elements. Spectral studies reveal some stars contain heavy elements that are relatively short lived—that is, these elements are unstable and break down in a comparatively short time. Their life span is far less than the stars in which they are found, leading to the conclusion that they had to be produced in those stars.

The other theory of element-building goes back to the "big bang" hypothesis discussed in Chapter II. In brief, it proposes that all of the material of the universe was at one time concentrated in a huge super atom which exploded, producing in a few minutes the kinds of atoms we know today. Proponents of this idea think the first theory fails because it requires more than one cooking pot; science, wherever possible, prefers the simpler hypothesis. But adherents of the stellar cooking idea believe the second theory could not result in buildup of the elements beyond helium. They also point to plenty of evidence that second-generation stars exist.

As noted earlier, hydrogen is the most abundant element anywhere we look in the universe. In the sun, the number of hydrogen atoms total more than all of the other kinds of atoms combined. Helium atoms are the next most plentiful. Beyond that, the numbers of more complex atoms decrease steadily with increasing atomic weight. This composition appears to be typical throughout space.

In Chapter III, we discussed the theory that planets start as lesser eddies within the cloud from which a star condenses, being, in effect, stillborn stars. If this is the case, planets must accompany the birth of many stars. One of the main pieces of evidence supporting this view is the fact that more than half of the stars condense as pairs, triplets, or even quadruplets rather than as lone bodies. The members of such systems move in orbits around each other at distances comparable to the distance of the major planets from the sun. These systems further resemble ours in that the members vary considerably in size; stellar giants may be mated with very tiny stars.

At the distances separating us from other stars we cannot hope to detect small, dark bodies in other systems by telescopes on the earth's surface. But they are believed to be there.

Scientists believe that life, too, must develop as part of the evolution of matter in the manner outlined in Chapter VIII. Although life could take many curious forms on other worlds, as shown by the great variety on earth, it seems almost a certainty that it would have to be based on the unique characteristics of the carbon atom. The conviction behind this statement stems from more than the mere fact that life on earth is dependent upon the action of this element. The carbon atom occupies a special place in the structure of life because of its great ability, more so than any other element, to combine with itself and other elements to build the extremely complicated molecules that life requires.

Life based upon other elements, such as silicon, which also is able to construct large molecules, seems unlikely, for no element can match carbon in building the numerous substances needed by living matter.

In considering how life may develop elsewhere, it is well to keep in mind the statement at the beginning of this chapter—that the laws and consequences of nature are the same everywhere. The same fundamental building blocks exist throughout the universe, and they can result in only one set of atoms. These atoms, being constructed in certain ways, can act only in certain ways, which is saying that the laws of chemistry are the same everywhere in space.

While some experts don't rule out the possibility that life elsewhere could be based on other elements, natural law rules that carbon-based life has a far greater chance of rising and flourishing than any other.

In the past, a popular idea has been that purely random processes could have accounted for development of life on earth. The essence of this argument is that if you throw nature's multifaceted dice often enough and long enough you are *bound* to hit a successful combination. In other words, the chance meeting and reaction of various substances in a primordial atmosphere and ocean eventually, over eons, will produce the primitive molecules from which life is able to develop.

This kind of appeal to our credulity is unnecessary in light of the order we see in nature—the basic building blocks and the nuclear and chemical rules they must follow. While random combinations of matter certainly must occur in the evolutionary process, it appears that they do not have far to proceed before selectivity begins to take a hand. Consider, for example, the phenomenon known as *autocatalysis* in which the substance resulting from a chemical transformation is catalytic, having the ability to influence the rate of its own formation.

Dr. Melvin Calvin, Department of Chemistry and Radiation Laboratory, University of California, finds it "surprising that this phenomenon was not utilized long ago in such discussions as these, since it is in essence the mechanism of all selective evolutionary processes."

Using the diagram in Figure 3, he points out that of three possible transformations which A might undergo—to B, C, or D—it will undergo more frequently the transformation to D because D is a better catalyst for that transformation than it is for the others. Eventually then, the random processes will not be so random in their future effect. They will tend to produce D at the expense of B and C. In this way, the most efficient process will eventually supersede the others.

This is the transformation catalyzed by D.

Figure 3. Autocatalysis as the means of chemical selection.

Selectivity is seen in the way in which large, flat molecules tend to arrange themselves when they come out of a solution in crystals. Being flat, these molecules conglomerate, not edge to edge, but with their flat surfaces in contact somewhat like a handful of poker chips spilled on the floor. It is in just such an arrangement of flat molecules that much of our genetic information is passed from parent to child.

Striking examples of how the large protein molecules in biological materials tend to collect into ordered arrays have been shown in experiments in which molecules of muscle fibers have been separated and mixed into random orientation in solution. Upon precipitating, these molecules reorient themselves to reproduce the pattern of the muscle fiber they originally formed. Large molecules carry many electric charges on their surfaces, and, therefore, are inclined to become aligned with each other somewhat like magnets.

If we accept the proposal that carbon must form the basis for living forms anywhere in the universe, we are led to the conclusion that life has the best chance of developing in those places where conditions generally fall within the range experienced in the ecosphere surrounding our own sun.* We cannot hope to find life developing on a planet that is as hot as boiling water or so cold that its water is perpetually frozen. The complex structure of living matter breaks

* This doesn't necessarily mean, however, that we can exclude all planets which fall outside the ecosphere, as indicated by the theory about Jupiter in Chapter X.

down easily under heat, and the chemical activity necessary for life processes cannot occur at extremely low temperatures. As for materials, all of the basic substances needed on earth must be present, including carbon, oxygen, hydrogen, and nitrogen, the four most chemically reactive elements and those which make up about 99 per cent of living matter. Oxygen is deemed essential to higher life forms because those on earth obtain their energy by the oxidation of carbon—oxygen is needed to "burn" an organism's food just as it is required to consume wood in a fireplace. Some low forms of life obtain their energy through fermentation, which is very inefficient compared to the process of combustion.

Although we demand these conditions, it doesn't follow that life on other worlds must duplicate ours. Quite a range remains possible, and relatively small differences in environment could produce kinds of life almost inconceivable to us. We have only to look around to see what a multitude of forms the carbon atom can produce.

Granting that conditions on planets may vary widely, as seen in our own solar system, the universe is so vast that the number of suitable planets could add up to a staggering total. One estimate is that in our galaxy alone, containing 100 billion stars, there may be 100,000 habitable planets. Since there are about one billion galaxies scattered as far as we can see (Plate 16), the number of such worlds could, perhaps, total 100,000 billion. A much more conservative estimate would cut this to 100 million, still a considerable number.

Eager to communicate with other beings in the universe, we have begun trying to detect intelligent signals in space by the only means available, the radio telescope. The theory behind this effort, started with an eighty-five-foot instrument at the U.S. National Radio Astronomy Observatory near Greenbank, West Virginia, is that other intelligent life may already have started beaming messages into space in search of us. Experts have given some thought to what

158

form these signals might take and have decided that they would consist of the universal language of numbers—perhaps a series of pulses reading simply, "1, 2, 3, 4 . . . 1, 2, 3, 4 . . ."

So far we have tried without success, in a project dubbed "Ozma," to pick up signals from several stars in our vicinity of the galaxy, including Tau Ceti, Epsilon Eridani, and Epsilon Indi, all within fifteen light years of earth. They are among the few neighboring stars that seem to meet the conditions deemed necessary for possession of habitable planets.

In general, these conditions have to do with a star's heat output, or luminosity; how long its output remains at a constant level, and whether it is a single body or a member of a double or multiple star system.

Astronomers, using some amazingly sensitive instruments, have been able to learn a great deal about stars and classify them into various types. They know that stars burn their fuel at different rates, depending in general upon their mass and composition. The largest and brightest burn fast and hot, using up their fuel supply and dying, perhaps in a planet-consuming explosion, in only a few million years. At the other extreme are relatively dim, cool stars that burn much more slowly and may have an active life of more than 100 billion years. Some stars rotate rapidly, others very slowly. During its lifetime a star goes through periods of contraction and expansion, and may increase its heat radiation manyfold. According to some experts, our own sun, as it uses up its hydrogen over some billions of years, will expand and become so hot that the earth's oceans will boil, killing all life. Following this, the sun will shrink again, eventually becoming a faint white dwarf star.

Most stars have been classified into spectral types designated by the letters, O, B, A, F, G, K, and M, representing a descending temperature scale, from about 500,000 degrees to only a few thousand degrees. Each type is broken into ten subdivisions, which results in a letter-numeral designation such as B1, F4, etc.

The stars which fall on this scale are called *main-sequence* stars and share a common characteristic: They have reached a state of equilibrium, a balance between the forces of contraction and expansion, which allows them to maintain a constant heat output. The time spent in this stage of evolution varies considerably among stars.

Lying in about the middle of the main sequence is our own sun, an average G2 star which may be five billion years old and have at least that much life ahead of it.

In searching the heavens for other stars best suited to life, the logical approach is to use the solar system as a yardstick since it seems reasonable to assume that it represents the cosmic average. First, we eliminate the fast-burning, short-lived stars, for our yardstick says that the average time necessary for life to develop as highly as ours—to the level where it has the technology to send or receive interstellar signals—is two to five billion years. We also eliminate those stars which might be expected to change their heat output by as much as 10 per cent during a period of two to five billion years. We could not survive such a change, either way, in our sun's radiation.

Double or multiple star systems cannot qualify since only under special circumstances could planets in such systems maintain stable orbits—paths which remain at all times within the habitable zone around a given star.

The result of this process of elimination, according to a study by Dr. Su-Shu Huang, University of California astrophysicist, is to narrow the choice down to F, G, and K stars.

At this point in our search a curious phenomenon suddenly presents itself, as if it were one of the missing pieces of a puzzle—rapid stellar rotation ceases abruptly below the F5 stars. Our sun is one of these slowly rotating stars. Most of the total energy of rotation, or angular momentum, of the solar system is possessed by the planets, with big Jupiter having the largest share, far more than the sun itself.

It seems to be the rule that young, hot stars spin rapidly, while others rotate slowly. Is this because the angular momentum of these latter stars has been absorbed by planets? It is tempting to think so. This is one of the mysteries we seek to solve in space.

INDEX

INDEX